WeightWatchers®
ProPoints® Plan

Freezer Friendly Meals

Delicious prepare ahead dishes
to fill your freezer

Kim Morphew

SIMON &
SCHUSTER
ILLUSTRATED

London · New York · Sydney · Toronto · New Delhi

A CBS COMPANY

First published in Great Britain by
Simon & Schuster UK Ltd, 2013
A CBS Company

Copyright © 2013, Weight Watchers International, Inc.

SIMON & SCHUSTER
ILLUSTRATED BOOKS
Simon & Schuster UK Ltd
222 Gray's Inn Road
London WC1X 8HB
www.simonandschuster.co.uk
Simon & Schuster Australia, Sydney
Simon & Schuster India, New Delhi

Weight Watchers, **ProPoints** and the **ProPoints** icon
are the registered trademarks of Weight Watchers
International Inc. and used under license by
Weight Watchers (UK) Ltd. All rights reserved.

Weight Watchers Publications Team: Lucy Clements,
Imogen Prescott, Nina McKerlie
Photography: Dan Jones
Food preparation: Kim Morphew
Prop styling: Rachel Jukes and Rebecca Newport
Front cover photography : Steve Baxter
Front cover food preparation : Sue Ashworth
Front cover prop styling : Jenny Iggleden

For Simon & Schuster Illustrated
Director of Illustrated Publishing: Ami Stewart
Senior Commissioning Editor: Nicky Hill
Art Director: Corinna Farrow
Production Manager: Katherine Thornton

Colour Reproduction by Dot Gradations Ltd, UK
Printed and bound in Italy

A CIP catalogue record for this book is available from
the British Library

ISBN: 978-1-47113-016-8

Pictured on front cover: Turkey Kiev, page 38, French fries,
page 104, Oven roasted rainbow veggies, page 102
Pictured on back cover from left to right: Beef and chorizo
one pot, page 40; Frozen raspberry terrine, page 136;
Satay turkey skewers, page 30; Aubergine cannelloni,
page 88
Pictured on front flap: Butternut squash and coconut curry,
page 83
Pictured on back flap: Herby toad in the hole, page 54

ProPoints ® value logo: You'll find this easy to read
ProPoints value logo on every recipe throughout this book.
The logo represents the number of **ProPoints** values per serving each
recipe contains. It is not an indication of the fillingness of a recipe.

The **ProPoints** plan is a flexible, simple and effective way for you to lose
weight and keep it off for good. The plan will allow you to enjoy lots of
delicious meals that fit around your lifestyle on your weight loss journey.

Filling & Healthy Foods are highlighted in green. Focus on these foods
where you can – they are healthy choices that will help you to feel satisfied
for longer.

This symbol denotes a vegetarian recipe and assumes that, where
relevant, free range eggs, vegetarian cheese, vegetarian virtually
fat-free fromage frais, vegetarian low fat crème fraîche and vegetarian low
fat yogurts are used. Virtually fat-free fromage frais, low fat crème fraîche
and low fat yogurts may contain traces of gelatine so they are not always
suitable for a vegetarian diet. Please check the labels.

Recipe notes

Egg size: medium unless otherwise stated.
Raw eggs: only the freshest eggs should be used. Pregnant women, the
elderly and children should avoid recipes with eggs which are not fully
cooked or raw.
All fruits and vegetables: medium size unless otherwise stated.
Chocolate: use chocolate with a minimum of 70% cocoa solids.
Low fat spread: where a recipe states to use a low fat spread, a light
spread with a fat content of no less than 38% should be used.
Stock: stock cubes should be used in the recipes, unless otherwise
stated. Prepare them according to the packet instructions, unless directed
otherwise.
Microwaves: microwave timings are for an 850 watt microwave oven.
Preparation and cooking times: these are approximate and meant to be
guidelines. Please note that the preparation time includes all the steps up
to and following the main cooking time(s).
Low fat soft cheese: where a recipe states to use low fat soft cheese, a
soft cheese with a fat content of less than 5% should be used.

Contents

Freezer Friendly Meals

We all know one of the most risky times when you're likely to blow your **ProPoints** budget: it's when the fridge is nearly empty, you haven't had time to go shopping and you're not sure what to cook. That's when it's all too easy to stop at the fish and chip shop on the way home or reach for the phone to order a pizza. But there's a really simple way to avoid falling into the takeaway trap and all those high **ProPoints** value options. With just a bit of forward planning you can stock your freezer with delicious meals ready to defrost and prepare in minutes.

What's inside this book?

Freezer Friendly Meals is packed with loads of tasty dishes that are perfect for freezing. You'll find vibrant Thai curries such as Thai Beef Mussaman, classic Italian Stuffed Chicken, Mediterranean-inspired Peperonata Cod, Tex-Mex style Chicken Enchiladas and good old-fashioned comfort foods like Herby Toad in the Hole. There really is something for everyone, from the adventurous cook who wants to make their own gnocchi, to straightforward soups and snacks.

Vegetarians can choose from dishes such as Caramelised Onion and Gorgonzola Tart or Sweet Potato and Goat's Cheese Rösti. There is also a brilliant selection of mouth-watering puddings, from Raspberry Sorbet to Pear Strudel, all perfect to whip out of the freezer and serve.

Cooking in batches

Every recipe tells you at which stage to freeze the dish and exactly how to do it. You might decide to set aside a Sunday afternoon to make and freeze a batch of dishes to free you up whenever you need a break in the

coming weeks. Or you might choose your favourite recipe and double it up – putting dinner on the table and a spare in the freezer in one easy go. When a recipe serves four but there are only two of you at home, try serving half for dinner and freezing the rest. Be creative and do whatever suits your situation and lifestyle.

Why should I do it?

The huge bonus of making your own frozen ready meals is that you know what's gone into them: good wholesome ingredients that are low in **ProPoints** values. And you'll find it's a much cheaper way to fill your freezer. Always label every dish clearly before you freeze it – you may think you'll recognise dishes easily, but it's not as easy as you think. And add the date too, so that you enjoy the dishes at their absolute delicious best. Write the **ProPoints** values on the lid and you'll know exactly which meals will fit in with your daily allowance; you could buy foil trays with cardboard lids which are easily available in the supermarket. Every recipe gives instructions on reheating dishes: many can be put straight into the oven from frozen so all you need worry about is getting the plates out of the cupboard.

Planned with ProPoints values

Whichever recipes you choose, the **ProPoints** values will have already been calculated, making it easy for you to track. This unique, flexible system enables you to plan and prepare the meals that suit your lifestyle – whether you're cooking for yourself, your family or friends – fitting in with all the demands of a normal, hectic life.

Quick ProPoints values index

0 ProPoints value
Roasted butternut squash soup **18**

1 ProPoints value
Carrot and swede crush **118**

2 ProPoints value
White bean saffron soup **16**

2 ProPoints value
Spanish tomato and chorizo soup **20**

2 ProPoints value
Asparagus, pea and pesto soup **22**

2 ProPoints value
Oven roasted rainbow veggies **102**

2 ProPoints value
Stir-fry veggies **119**

2 ProPoints value
Raspberry sorbet **138**

3 ProPoints value
Sticky glazed pork kebabs **52**

3 ProPoints value
French fries **104**

3 ProPoints value
Parmesan potatoes **108**

3 ProPoints value
Onion rings **112**

3 ProPoints value
Cheesy potato skins **116**

3 ProPoints value
Frozen raspberry terrine **136**

4 ProPoints value
Baked scampi **64**

4 ProPoints value
Peperonata cod **66**

4 ProPoints value
Butternut squash and coconut curry **82**

4 ProPoints value
Rosemary focaccia **114**

4 ProPoints value
Creamy mashed potato **118**

4 ProPoints value
Normandy apple tarts **124**

4 ProPoints value
Chocolate and cherry pavlovas **126**

4 ProPoints value
Apple crumble and mincemeat fingers **128**

4 ProPoints value
St Clement's sponge pudding **130**

4 ProPoints value
Simple pear strudel **134**

4 ProPoints value
Arctic roll **140**

5 ProPoints value
Creamy chicken and ham soup **12**

ProPoints					
5 Chicken and aubergine masala **36**	**5** Hot and peppery fish cakes **60**	**5** Aubergine cannelloni **88**	**5** Spicy bean burgers **94**	**5** Cheesy leeks and ham **100**	**5** Self-saucing chocolate pudding **132**
6 Italian stuffed chicken **26**	**6** Must-try pepper crust fillet steak **42**	**6** Twice-baked cheese soufflés **80**	**6** Pilau rice **106**	**6** Dauphinoise potatoes **110**	**7** Chicken pot noodle soup **10**
7 Beef chilli soup **14**	**7** Chicken and chestnut mushroom lasagne **28**	**7** Chianti chicken **34**	**7** The nicest sweet potato and goat's cheese rösti **78**	**8** Beef and chorizo one pot **40**	**8** Herby toad in the hole **54**
8 Home-made spinach gnocchi **92**	**9** Satay turkey skewers **30**	**9** Easy enchiladas **32**	**9** Turkey Kiev **38**	**9** Prawn pepper tartlets **68**	**9** Smoked haddock and sweet potato gratin **72**
9 Seafood linguine **74**	**9** Thai sticky rice **96**	**10** Individual steak pies **44**	**10** Parma ham and pesto pizza **56**	**10** Salmon en croûte **62**	**10** Caramelised onion and Gorgonzola tart **84**
11 Roasted pepper lamb pasta **48**	**11** Chorizo and soya bean risotto **50**	**11** Italian pasta bake **86**	**11** Giant samosas **90**	**12** Thai beef mussaman **46**	**13** Salmon and couscous parcels **70**

Freezer Friendly Meals Quick ProPoints values index 7

"I always have a batch of soup in the freezer and I plan, plan, plan!

Dawn Lindsey McNaught Weight Watchers member

Soups

Chicken pot noodle soup

This is brilliant to take to work – defrost overnight, then at lunchtime just pour over some boiling water for an instant soup.

ProPoints values per serving	
ProPoints values per recipe	29
Serves 4	

 20 minutes in total

150 g (5½ oz) dried quick-cook medium
   egg noodles, broken roughly
a kettleful of boiling water
calorie controlled cooking spray
1 onion, chopped finely
1 teaspoon dried Chinese five spice
a pinch of chilli flakes
1 vegetable stock cube, crumbled
1 tablespoon tomato purée
198 g can sweetcorn, drained
150 g (5½ oz) cooked skinless chicken
   breast, shredded
1 litre (1¾ pints) boiling water
coriander sprigs, to garnish (optional)
a few sliced spring onions, to garnish
   (optional)

1 Put the noodles in a large bowl and cover with boiling water. Set aside for 5 minutes then drain in a colander, rinse with cold water and drain again. Set aside.

2 Meanwhile, heat a large non-stick saucepan over a medium heat and spray with the cooking spray. Cook the onion for 3–4 minutes until softened, stirring occasionally.

3 Add the Chinese five spice, chilli flakes, stock cube, tomato purée, sweetcorn, chicken and soaked noodles to the cooked onions and cook for 1 minute, stirring to combine everything.

4 Pour in the litre of boiling water and simmer gently for 1–2 minutes, until the noodles are tender. Serve in bowls, garnished with coriander sprigs and spring onion, if desired.

Freezing

At the end of step 3, divide the chicken mixture equally between foil trays or containers. Leave to go cold. Seal, label and freeze for up to 3 months.

Serving

Defrost a portion of the chicken mixture and put it into a bowl or mug. Pour over 250 ml (9 fl oz) boiling water and leave to stand for 5 minutes. Stir and serve immediately. Or, if you are serving more than one portion, put in a saucepan and cook as per step 4.

> Cook's tip Serve each portion with a 60 g (2 oz) slice of French stick to soak up the delicious juices, for an extra 4 ProPoints values per serving.

Creamy chicken and ham soup

This is a real meal-in-a-soup, so perfect for lunch or even a low **ProPoints** values light dinner.

ProPoints values per serving

ProPoints values per recipe **19**

Serves 4

 25 minutes in total

calorie controlled cooking spray

1 onion, chopped roughly

2 celery sticks, chopped roughly

1 carrot, peeled and chopped roughly

½ teaspoon dried tarragon

500 ml (18 fl oz) hot chicken stock

35 g (1¼ oz) slice wholemeal bread, torn
    roughly

200 g tub low fat soft cheese

200 g (7 oz) cooked skinless chicken
    breast, shredded

100 g (3½ oz) frozen peas

50 g (1¾ oz) lean ham, diced

salt and freshly ground black pepper

1 Heat a large lidded saucepan over a medium heat and spray with the cooking spray. Cook the onion, celery, carrot and tarragon for 10 minutes, covered, until softened, stirring occasionally.

2 Add the chicken stock and bring to the boil. Stir in the bread and soft cheese and whizz the soup with a hand-held blender, or transfer to a blender in batches, and whizz until smooth.

3 Return to the saucepan and season generously. Add the chicken, peas and ham and bring to a simmer. Cook for 5 minutes until the peas are tender and the soup is hot.

Freezing

Divide the soup equally between foil trays or containers. Leave to go cold. Seal, label and freeze for up to 3 months.

Serving

Defrost the soup then put in a saucepan and reheat on a low heat for 5–7 minutes until piping hot, stirring occasionally until smooth. Alternatively, microwave on high for 4 minutes, stirring halfway through. Leave to stand for 1 minute before serving.

Beef chilli soup

What better soup to serve on Bonfire Night than chilli con carne in a bowl? Bursting with flavour and spices, this will soon become a family favourite.

ProPoints values per serving	**7** ProPoints value
ProPoints values per recipe	27
Serves 4	

20 minutes preparation
15 minutes cooking

calorie controlled cooking spray

250 g (9 oz) extra lean beef mince

1 onion**, diced finely**

39 g sachet chilli con carne spice mix

400 g can chopped tomatoes

300 ml (10 fl oz) beef stock

100 g (3½ oz) dried long grain rice

a handful of fresh coriander **leaves,**
    reserving a few for garnish

salt and freshly ground black pepper

4 tablespoons reduced fat sour cream,
    to serve

1 Heat a large lidded saucepan and spray with the cooking spray. Cook the beef mince, onion and spices for 5 minutes over a medium-high heat until browned all over, stirring continuously.

2 Add the tomatoes, stock and rice and bring to the boil. Reduce the heat, cover and simmer for 15 minutes until the rice is tender. Stir through the coriander, check the seasoning and serve garnished with the sour cream and the reserved coriander.

Freezing

Divide the soup equally between foil trays or containers. Leave to go cold. Seal, label and freeze for up to 3 months.

Serving

Defrost the soup then put in a saucepan and reheat on a low heat for 5–7 minutes until piping hot, stirring occasionally until smooth. Or microwave on high for 4 minutes, stirring halfway through. Leave to stand for 1 minute before serving.

White bean saffron soup

A delicious, filling soup with the added bonus that it's quick to prepare. Serve each portion with a 60 g (2 oz) slice of French stick for an extra 4 **ProPoints** values per serving.

ProPoints values per serving	2 ProPoints value
ProPoints values per recipe	18
Serves 8	

🕐 20 minutes in total

calorie controlled cooking spray
1 onion, chopped roughly
3 celery sticks, chopped roughly
1 large carrot, peeled and chopped roughly
a pinch of saffron threads
2 × 400 g cans cannellini beans in water, drained and rinsed
1 litre (1¾ pints) hot vegetable stock
125 g (4½ oz) half fat crème fraîche
1 small red chilli, de-seeded and diced finely
a few fresh coriander leaves
salt and freshly ground black pepper

1 Heat a large lidded saucepan over a medium heat and spray with the cooking spray. Cook the onion, celery and carrots for 5–8 minutes, covered, until softened, stirring occasionally.

2 Add the saffron, cannellini beans and vegetable stock and bring to the boil. Reduce the heat and simmer for 5 minutes. Add the crème fraîche and whizz with a hand-held blender or transfer to a blender and whizz until smooth.

3 Return to the saucepan, reheat if necessary and check the seasoning. Serve topped with the chilli and coriander.

Freezing

At the end of step 2, divide the soup equally between foil trays or containers. Leave to go cold. Seal, label and freeze for up to 3 months.

Serving

Defrost the soup then put in a saucepan and reheat on a low heat for 5–7 minutes until piping hot, stirring occasionally until smooth. Alternatively, microwave on high for 4 minutes, stirring halfway through. Leave to stand for 1 minute before serving, sprinkled with the diced chilli and coriander leaves.

Roasted butternut squash soup

By cooking the vegetables in the oven, you intensify their flavour and bring out their natural sweetness. Serve each portion with a 60 g (2 oz) wholemeal bread roll per person for an extra 4 **ProPoints** values per serving.

ProPoints values per serving	
ProPoints values per recipe	0
Serves 6	

15 minutes preparation
45 minutes cooking

1 red onion**, chopped**

1 garlic clove**, halved**

1 fresh rosemary **sprig, leaves only, reserving a little for garnish**

800 g (1 lb 11 oz) butternut squash**, peeled, de-seeded and cut into small chunks**

2 carrots**, peeled and chopped roughly**

½ swede**, peeled and chopped roughly**

calorie controlled cooking spray

1 litre (1¾ pints) boiling water

salt and freshly ground black pepper

1 Preheat the oven to Gas Mark 5/190°C/fan oven 170°C. Put the onion, garlic, rosemary, squash, carrots and swede on a large non-stick baking tray and spray generously with the cooking spray. Roast in the oven for 45 minutes until golden and tender, stirring halfway through.

2 Transfer the vegetables to a blender and whizz in batches with a little of the boiling water until smooth. Transfer the purée to a large saucepan and add the remaining water. Or, using a hand-held blender, whizz the vegetables with all the water in a large pan until smooth. Gently heat the soup until just before boiling, check the seasoning and serve, garnished with the reserved rosemary leaves, chopped, and a sprinkling of black pepper.

Freezing

Divide the soup equally between foil trays or containers. Leave to go cold. Seal, label and freeze for up to 3 months.

Serving

Defrost the soup then put in a saucepan and reheat on a low heat for 5–7 minutes until piping hot, stirring occasionally until smooth. Alternatively, microwave on high for 4 minutes, stirring halfway through. Leave to stand for 1 minute before serving.

Spanish tomato and chorizo soup

Chorizo and saffron give this a real Spanish twist. Serve each portion with a 25 g (1 oz) slice of reduced fat garlic bread for an extra 3 **ProPoints** values per serving.

ProPoints values per serving	**2** ProPoints value
ProPoints values per recipe	**10**
Serves 4	

 30 minutes in total

calorie controlled cooking spray
100 g (3½ oz) chorizo, diced finely
1 onion, chopped finely
1 garlic clove, crushed
a pinch of saffron threads
2 × 400 g cans chopped tomatoes
300 ml (10 fl oz) hot chicken stock
2 teaspoons caster sugar
100 g (3½ oz) roasted red peppers from a
     jar, drained and diced
salt and freshly ground black pepper

1 Heat a large lidded saucepan over a medium heat and spray with the cooking spray. Cook the chorizo for 2–3 minutes until very lightly browned, then remove with a slotted spoon to a plate. Add the onion and cook for 3–4 minutes, covered, until starting to soften, stirring occasionally. Add the garlic and saffron and cook for a further 3 minutes.

2 Stir in the tomatoes, stock and sugar, bring to the boil, reduce the heat and simmer for 10 minutes. With a hand-held blender, whizz the soup until about half is smooth, or transfer half to a blender and whizz. Return to the saucepan and stir in the chorizo and red pepper. Reheat if necessary, check the seasoning, then serve.

Freezing

Divide the soup equally between foil trays or containers. Leave to go cold. Seal, label and freeze for up to 3 months.

Serving

Defrost the soup then put in a saucepan and reheat on a low heat for 5–7 minutes until piping hot, stirring occasionally until smooth. Alternatively, microwave on high for 4 minutes, stirring halfway through. Leave to stand for 1 minute before serving.

Asparagus, pea and pesto soup

Serve each portion with 25 g (1 oz) of reduced fat breadsticks for a tasty lunch and an extra 3 **ProPoints** values per serving.

ProPoints values per serving	
ProPoints values per recipe	**19**
Serves 8	

2 ProPoints value

🕐 25 minutes in total

calorie controlled cooking spray
2 onions**, chopped**
2 tablespoons plain flour
1 litre (1¾ pints) hot vegetable stock
500 g (1 lb 2 oz) asparagus**, woody ends**
**   discarded, chopped roughly**
250 g (9 oz) frozen peas
50 g (1¾ oz) pesto
salt and freshly ground black pepper

1 Heat a large lidded saucepan over a medium heat and spray with the cooking spray. Add the onions and cook for 10 minutes, covered, until softened, stirring occasionally, until lightly browned.

2 Add the flour and cook for 30 seconds, stirring, then gradually pour in the stock, stirring until combined, with no lumps. Bring to the boil, then reduce the heat and simmer for 2 minutes. Add the asparagus and peas, bring back to the boil and simmer for 3 minutes.

3 Season and then whizz until smooth with a hand-held blender or transfer to a blender in batches and whizz. Reheat if necessary in the saucepan. Serve in bowls, with a sprinkling of black pepper and a swirl of pesto on the top.

Freezing

Divide the soup equally between foil trays or containers. Leave to go cold. Seal, label and freeze for up to 3 months.

Serving

Defrost the soup then put in a saucepan and reheat on a low heat for 5–7 minutes until piping hot, stirring occasionally until smooth. Alternatively, microwave on high for 4 minutes, stirring halfway through. Leave to stand for 1 minute before serving.

"Double up and freeze for those evenings when you just don't have time to cook. That way you avoid the urge to order takeaways."

Sarah De-Ste-Croix Weight Watchers member

Chicken, Turkey + Meat

Italian stuffed chicken

This makes a fantastic roast dinner whether it's a special occasion or not. Serve with 100 g (3½ oz) dry roasted potatoes per person, cooked carrots and green beans for 2 extra **ProPoints** values per serving. It's also good with chicken gravy made with 2 teaspoons chicken gravy granules per person for an extra 1 **ProPoints** value per serving.

ProPoints values per serving	
ProPoints values per recipe	35
Serves 6	

 25 minutes preparation
1 hour cooking

calorie controlled cooking spray

1 red onion, chopped finely

500 g (1 lb 2 oz) skinless, boneless chicken breasts

8 × 7 g (¼ oz) rashers pancetta

4 × 39 g (1½ oz) Weight Watchers Premium Pork Sausages

50 g (1¾ oz) dried breadcrumbs

2 tablespoons finely chopped fresh flat leaf parsley

45 g (1½ oz) red pesto

salt and freshly ground black pepper

1 Preheat the oven to Gas Mark 5/190°C/fan oven 170°C. Heat a non-stick saucepan over a medium heat and spray with the cooking spray. Cook the onion for 5 minutes until softened. Remove and put in a bowl. Leave to go cold.

2 Meanwhile, cover a chopping board with a large piece of cling film. Cut a chicken breast through the centre horizontally and open out like a butterfly. Put on the cling film and cover with another piece of cling film. Bash with the end of a rolling pin until it is about 1 cm (½ inch) thick. Repeat with the remaining chicken breasts.

3 Arrange the pancetta slices on a large piece of foil in a line, about 1 cm (½ inch) apart. Put the chicken breasts in a line on top, slightly overlapping the edges, to make a large rectangle. Remove the skins from the sausages and add to the cooked onion with the breadcrumbs, parsley and some seasoning.

4 Spread the red pesto along the chicken breasts, then spoon the stuffing on top to make a large sausage in the centre of the chicken. Using the foil to help, roll up the chicken from one of the long edges to make a large joint. Seal the foil tightly.

5 Transfer the foil parcel to a baking tray and then bake in the oven for 45 minutes. Carefully remove the foil and discard. Return the chicken to the oven for a further 10–15 minutes until it is golden and the juices run clear. Carve the chicken into slices and serve 150 g (5½ oz) per person.

Freezing

At the end of step 4, put the wrapped chicken joint in a freezer bag, seal, label and freeze for up to 3 months.

Serving

Defrost thoroughly and then cook as per step 5 until golden and cooked through.

Cook's tip If you don't have red pesto you can use green pesto instead, for the same **ProPoints** values per serving.

Chicken and chestnut mushroom lasagne

This creamy lasagne is a crowd pleaser and makes a real change from the traditional version.

ProPoints values per serving	**7** ProPoints value
ProPoints values per recipe	42
Serves 6	

45 minutes preparation
45 minutes cooking

calorie controlled cooking spray
3 leeks, sliced thinly and rinsed
500 g (1 lb 2 oz) skinless, boneless
  chicken breasts, cut into 1 cm
    (½ inch) cubes
2 teaspoons dried tarragon
200 g (7 oz) chestnut mushrooms, sliced
2 garlic cloves, crushed
200 g (7 oz) baby spinach, chopped
600 ml (20 fl oz) skimmed milk
2 tablespoons cornflour
200 g tub low fat soft cheese
6 × 20 g (¾ oz) dried lasagne sheets
25 g (1 oz) Parmesan cheese, grated
salt and freshly ground black pepper

1 Preheat the oven to Gas Mark 4/180°C/fan oven 160°C. Heat a non-stick wide, lidded saucepan over a medium heat and spray with the cooking spray. Cook the leeks with 2 tablespoons of water, covered, for 10 minutes, until softened and lightly coloured. Transfer to a bowl. Spray the pan again, add the chicken and cook for 10 minutes until lightly browned and cooked through. Remove with a slotted spoon and add to the leeks along with the tarragon and some seasoning. Set aside.

2 Heat the pan again over a medium heat and spray with the cooking spray. Cook the mushrooms for 10 minutes, covered, until softened and lightly browned. Add the garlic and spinach and cook for 2 minutes until the spinach has wilted. Increase the heat to boil off any liquid. Season and set aside.

3 In a jug, mix 2 tablespoons of the milk with the cornflour to make a paste. Add the remaining milk and stir to combine. Transfer to a non-stick saucepan along with the soft cheese and gently heat until boiling, stirring until smooth. Cook for 1 minute until thickened, season and set aside.

4 Spoon one third of the cheese sauce into the bottom of a 1 litre (1¾ pint) ovenproof dish. Top with half the spinach mixture. Arrange 3 lasagne sheets on top, then top with all the chicken mixture and another third of the cheese sauce. Top with the remaining lasagne sheets, the spinach and then the remaining cheese sauce. Scatter over the Parmesan cheese.

5 Bake the lasagne in the oven for 40–45 minutes until it is golden and bubbling and the pasta is cooked. Serve immediately.

Freezing

At the end of step 5, wrap and seal the lasagne with foil. Label and freeze for up to 3 months.

Serving

Defrost and cook as per step 5 until golden and bubbling. Once defrosted, there is no need to cover it when baking.

Satay turkey skewers

Serve this Eastern-inspired dish with 100 g (3½ oz) new potatoes per person and a mixed salad for an extra 2 **ProPoints** values per serving.

ProPoints values per 2 skewers	
ProPoints values per recipe	37
Makes 8 skewers	

 40 minutes in total

juice and zest of 1 lime

2 tablespoons sweet chilli sauce

2 tablespoons chopped fresh coriander

1 tablespoon sesame oil

4 tablespoons light soy sauce

500 g (1 lb 2 oz) skinless turkey breast steaks, cut into strips

45 g (1½ oz) reduced fat smooth peanut butter

400 ml can reduced fat coconut milk

1 In a bowl, mix together the lime zest and juice, chilli sauce, coriander, sesame oil, 2 tablespoons of the soy sauce and the turkey breast strips, until combined. Set aside for 30 minutes.

2 Meanwhile, in a small pan, gently heat the peanut butter, the remaining soy sauce and the coconut milk until combined and smooth. Bubble for 8–10 minutes until thickened.

3 Preheat the grill to medium hot. Thread the marinated chunks of turkey on to eight metal or wooden skewers (see Cook's tip). Discard the remaining marinade. Cook the satay skewers under the grill for 5–8 minutes, turning until cooked through. Serve immediately with the satay sauce.

Freezing

At the end of step 1, divide the turkey equally between freezer bags or containers. Then at the end of step 2, leave the sauce to go cold and divide equally between foil trays or containers. Seal, label and freeze for up to 3 months.

Serving

Defrost both, cook the turkey as per step 3 until piping hot and warm the sauce in a small pan.

Cook's tip If using wooden skewers, they will need to be soaked in water for 30 minutes before using, or wrap the exposed ends in foil before grilling.

Easy chicken enchiladas

Serve each enchilada with a crisp Little Gem salad, some chopped tomatoes, thinly sliced red onion and 1 tablespoon each of reduced fat soured cream and reduced fat guacamole per person for 2 **ProPoints** values per serving.

ProPoints values per serving	9 ProPoints value
ProPoints values per recipe	37
Serves 4	

 30 minutes preparation
20 minutes cooking

calorie controlled cooking spray
500 g (1 lb 2 oz) skinless, boneless chicken breasts**, cut into small cubes**
1 red onion**, chopped**
1 red pepper**, de-seeded and sliced**
1 yellow pepper**, de-seeded and sliced**
30 g sachet fajita seasoning mix
400 g can chopped tomatoes
4 tablespoons tomato ketchup
4 × 42 g (1½ oz) tortilla wraps
100 g (3½ oz) reduced fat Cheddar cheese, grated
a handful of fresh coriander **leaves**
salt and freshly ground black pepper

1 Preheat the oven to Gas Mark 5/190°C/fan oven 170°C. Heat a non-stick frying pan over a medium heat and spray with the cooking spray. Cook the chicken, onion and peppers for 10 minutes, stirring. Sprinkle over the fajita seasoning mix and continue to cook for 5–7 minutes until the chicken is cooked through. Set aside.

2 Mix together the chopped tomatoes, ketchup and some seasoning. Pour into a 1 litre (1¾ pint) shallow ovenproof dish.

3 Put a tortilla wrap on a chopping board and spoon a quarter of the chicken filling along the middle. Roll up the wrap to enclose the filling and arrange in the ovenproof dish on top of the tomatoes. Repeat with the remaining filling and wraps. Sprinkle over the cheese.

4 Bake in the oven for 20 minutes until golden and bubbling. Serve scattered with the coriander.

Freezing

At the end of step 3, leave to go cold, then wrap, seal, label and freeze for up to 3 months.

Serving

Defrost and cook as per step 4 until piping hot.

Chianti chicken

This rich red wine chicken casserole is delicious served with the Creamy Mashed Potato on page 118 for an extra 4 **ProPoints** values.

7 ProPoints value	
ProPoints values per serving	
ProPoints values per recipe	**26**
Serves 4	

 30 minutes preparation
1½ hours cooking

calorie controlled cooking spray
500 g (1 lb 2 oz) skinless, boneless
   chicken breasts**, each sliced into**
   3 pieces
1 red onion**, chopped**
2 garlic cloves**, sliced**
1 tablespoon plain flour
125 ml (4 fl oz) Chianti red wine
1 tablespoon tomato purée
300 ml (10 fl oz) chicken stock
2 bay leaves
3 fresh thyme **sprigs**
400 g can cannellini beans in water**,**
   drained and rinsed
25 g (1 oz) stoned black olives in brine,
   halved
25 g (1 oz) sun-dried tomatoes, chopped
salt and freshly ground black pepper

1 Preheat the oven to Gas Mark 4/180°C/fan oven 160°C. Heat a flame and ovenproof lidded casserole dish over a high heat and spray with the cooking spray. Cook the chicken in batches, for 5 minutes per batch, until lightly browned. Remove and set aside.

2 Spray the pan again and cook the onion over a medium heat, covered, for 5–8 minutes until softened. Add the garlic and cook for 1 minute. Return the chicken to the pan and sprinkle with the flour. Cook for 1 minute, stirring, then add the wine and bubble for 30 seconds. Gradually stir in the tomato purée and add the chicken stock, stirring until smooth. Add the bay leaves and thyme, cover and cook in the oven for 45 minutes.

3 Remove from the oven and stir in the cannellini beans, olives and tomatoes. Return to the oven for a further 45 minutes until the chicken is tender and the sauce has thickened. Check the seasoning, discard the herbs and serve immediately.

Freezing

At the end of step 3, divide equally between foil trays or containers. Leave to go cold. Seal, label and freeze for up to 3 months.

Serving

Defrost and reheat on a low heat for 5–7 minutes until piping hot, stirring occasionally. Or microwave on high for 4 minutes, stirring halfway through. Leave to stand for 1 minute before serving.

Chicken and aubergine masala

Why not serve this fantastic curry, as we've done, with the home-made Pilau Rice on page 106 for an extra 6 *ProPoints* values per serving – a complete Indian feast.

ProPoints values per serving	
ProPoints values per recipe	**28**
Serves 6	

 20 minutes preparation
30 minutes cooking

calorie controlled cooking spray

6 × 150 g (5½ oz) skinless, boneless chicken breasts**, cut into bite size chunks**

1 aubergine**, trimmed and cut into small cubes**

1 onion**, chopped**

750 ml (1¼ pint) portion frozen Basic Curry Sauce (page 121), defrosted (or see Cook's tip)

200 g (7 oz) baby spinach

1 Heat a wide, lidded saucepan over a high heat and spray with the cooking spray. Cook the chicken chunks, in batches, for 5 minutes, until browned all over. Remove and set aside on a plate.

2 Spray the pan again, add the aubergine and onion, reduce the heat to medium and cook for 10 minutes until starting to brown. Return the chicken to the pan and add the curry sauce. Bring to the boil, then reduce the heat and simmer for 20 minutes. Add the spinach and stir to wilt. Serve in bowls immediately.

Freezing

At the end of step 2, divide equally between foil trays or containers. Leave to go cold. Seal, label and freeze for up to 3 months.

Serving

Defrost and reheat on a low heat for 5–7 minutes until piping hot, stirring occasionally, or microwave on high for 4 minutes, stirring halfway through. Leave to stand for 1 minute before serving.

Cook's tip **If you don't have any Basic Curry Sauce ready in the freezer, then in step 2, after you return the chicken, stir in 4 tablespoons tikka masala curry paste, 150 g (5½ oz) low fat soft cheese and 500 ml (18 fl oz) chicken stock instead. Bring to the boil, reduce the heat, then cover and simmer for 20 minutes. Stir through the spinach to wilt and serve for 7 ProPoints values per serving.**

Turkey Kiev

This turkey version of the classic Kiev makes for brilliant comfort food straight from the freezer.

ProPoints values per serving	**9** ProPoints value
ProPoints values per recipe	34
Serves 4	

20 minutes preparation
30 minutes cooking

4 × 150 g (5½ oz) **skinless turkey breast steaks**

150 g (5½ oz) **low fat soft cheese**

2 **garlic cloves, crushed**

4 tablespoons finely chopped **fresh flat leaf parsley**

4 × 17 g (½ oz) **slices Parma ham**

2 tablespoons plain flour

1 **egg, beaten**

100 g (3½ oz) **fresh breadcrumbs**

calorie controlled cooking spray

salt and freshly ground black pepper

1 Preheat the oven to Gas Mark 5/190°C/fan oven 170°C and put a baking tray in the oven to heat. Line a chopping board with cling film and put the turkey steaks on top. Put another sheet of cling film on top and bash the steaks with the end of a rolling pin until flattened to 5 mm (¼ inch).

2 In a bowl, mix together the soft cheese, garlic, parsley and some seasoning. Spread a quarter of this mixture on a turkey steak and then roll up the turkey to seal in the filling. Wrap the turkey roll with a piece of Parma ham to secure, tucking the ends under. Repeat with the remaining filling and turkey steaks.

3 Put the flour on a plate, the egg in a shallow bowl and the breadcrumbs on another plate. Dip each turkey roll into the flour, then the egg and finally roll in the breadcrumbs to coat completely. Repeat with the remaining turkey rolls.

4 Put the turkey Kievs on the preheated baking tray, spray with the cooking spray and bake in the oven for 30 minutes until golden and cooked through.

Freezing

At the end of step 3, wrap each turkey Kiev in cling film. Then put them in a freezer bag, seal, label and freeze for up to 3 months.

Serving

Defrost thoroughly and then cook as per step 4 until golden and cooked through.

Beef and chorizo one pot

This rich casserole is full of flavour and ideal for freezing in batches. Serve with sugar snap peas and tenderstem broccoli for no extra **ProPoints** values per serving.

ProPoints values per serving	**8** ProPoints value
ProPoints values per recipe	**51**
Serves 6	

🕐 30 minutes preparation
1¾ hours cooking

calorie controlled cooking spray
100 g (3½ oz) chorizo, cut into
    small cubes
2 onions, chopped
2 garlic cloves, crushed
750 g (1 lb 10 oz) lean stewing steak,
    cut into 2.5 cm (1 inch) cubes
2 tablespoons plain flour
125 ml (4 fl oz) red wine
500 ml (18 fl oz) hot beef stock
400 g can chopped tomatoes
3 fresh thyme sprigs
2 bay leaves
500 g (1 lb 2 oz) butternut squash,
    peeled, de-seeded and cut into
    2.5 cm (1 inch) cubes
600 g (1 lb 5 oz) large Charlotte or
    Desirée potatoes, peeled and cut
    into 2.5 cm (1 inch) cubes
salt and freshly ground black pepper

1 Preheat the oven to Gas Mark 3/170°C/fan oven 150°C. Heat a large lidded flame and ovenproof casserole dish over a medium heat and spray with the cooking spray. Cook the chorizo and onions for 10 minutes, covered, until softened. Add the garlic and cook for 1 minute, then transfer the mixture to a plate.

2 Spray the pan again and cook the beef in batches for 5 minutes, until browned all over. Return the chorizo and onions to the pan and sprinkle over the flour. Cook for 1 minute, stirring, then gradually add the red wine and bubble for 1 minute until reduced.

3 Pour in 300 ml (10 fl oz) of the beef stock and the chopped tomatoes, thyme and bay leaves, then season. Bring to the boil, cover and place in the oven for 1 hour.

4 Remove from the oven and add the remaining hot stock, butternut squash and potatoes, return to the oven and cook for a further 45 minutes until the beef and vegetables are tender. Check the seasoning, discard the herbs and serve sprinkled with black pepper.

Freezing

At the end of step 4, divide equally between foil trays or containers then leave to go cold. Seal, label and freeze for up to 3 months.

Serving

Defrost and reheat on a low heat for 5–7 minutes until piping hot, stirring occasionally. Alternatively, microwave on high for 4 minutes, stirring halfway through. Leave to stand for 1 minute before serving.

Must-try pepper crust fillet steak

Serve with the Carrot and Swede Crush on page 118 and some tenderstem broccoli for an extra 1 **ProPoints** value per serving.

6 ProPoints value

ProPoints values per serving	
ProPoints values per recipe	**26**
Serves 4	

 25 minutes in total

4 × 150 g (5½ oz) lean fillet steaks
30 black peppercorns
50 g (1¾ oz) wholemeal bread
2 tablespoons chopped fresh flat leaf parsley
15 g (½ oz) dried wild mushrooms, chopped finely
2 teaspoons Dijon mustard
calorie controlled cooking spray

1 Preheat the oven to Gas Mark 6/200°C/fan oven 180°C and put a non-stick baking tray in the oven to heat. Put the steaks on a board lined with cling film, put another sheet of cling film on top, and then bash the steaks with the end of a rolling pin until they are 1 cm (½ inch) thick.

2 In a pestle and mortar, finely crush the peppercorns. Put the peppercorns in a bowl with the bread, parsley and mushrooms. Whizz the mixture with a hand-held blender until it resembles coarse breadcrumbs, then put on a plate. Alternatively, use a food processor.

3 Brush the steaks on one side with the mustard and then press the brushed sides into the breadcrumb mixture until they are heavily coated.

4 Spray the steaks all over with the cooking spray, then transfer to the preheated baking tray, breadcrumb sides up, and cook in the oven for 6–8 minutes for medium rare or 10 minutes for well done. Serve immediately.

Freezing

At the end of step 3, wrap each of the steaks in a piece of cling film and put in freezer bags or containers. Seal, label and freeze for up to 3 months.

Serving

Defrost and cook as in step 4 until golden and piping hot.

Cook's tip Breadcrumbs can be frozen for up to 3 months, so why not whizz your leftover pieces of bread into fine crumbs, then freeze in portions in freezer bags?

Individual steak pies

These individual pies are perfect for freezing as their unusual shape keeps everything contained in a little parcel – and the dough doesn't take long at all to make from scratch.

ProPoints values per serving	
ProPoints values per recipe	**58**
Serves 6	

 35 minutes preparation
30 minutes cooking

calorie controlled cooking spray
200 g (7 oz) chestnut mushrooms**, wiped,**
**   trimmed and halved**
1 large red onion**, chopped finely**
2 garlic cloves**, crushed**
350 g (12 oz) strong bread flour
125 g tub quark
600 g (1 lb 5 oz) lean fillet steak**, cut into**
**   2.5 cm (1 inch) cubes**
2 tablespoons Worcestershire sauce
salt and freshly ground black pepper

1 Heat a non-stick frying pan over a medium heat and spray with the cooking spray. Cook the mushrooms and onion for 5–8 minutes until softened and starting to brown. Add the garlic and cook for 1 minute, then transfer to a bowl and leave to go cold.

2 Meanwhile, make the dough. Put the flour and a pinch of salt into a large bowl. Add the quark and gradually add about 100 ml (4 fl oz) cold water, mixing to make a smooth and soft, but not sticky, dough. Add a splash more water if too dry. Add the beef and Worcestershire sauce to the other bowl with the cooled mushrooms and toss to coat. Season generously.

3 Preheat the oven to Gas Mark 5/190°C/170°C fan oven. Divide the dough into six equal pieces. Roll one piece into an 18 cm (7 inch) circle. Spoon one sixth of the beef filling into the centre of the circle. Pull up the sides of the dough to the centre, pleating over the pastry and pressing together in the centre. Transfer to a baking sheet lined with non-stick baking parchment and repeat with the remaining dough and filling. Spray the pies with a little of the cooking spray.

4 Bake the pies in the oven for 30 minutes until golden and cooked, then serve.

Freezing

At the end of step 3, open freeze the pies on a baking tray for 4–6 hours until frozen. Then wrap each in cling film and put into freezer bags or containers. Seal, label and freeze for up to 3 months.

Serving

Defrost and cook as in step 4 until golden and piping hot.

> **Variation** Why not add 50 g (1¾ oz) crumbled Stilton or Gorgonzola cheese to the beef for a piquant twist, for 11 *ProPoints* values per serving? You could also add fresh thyme, rosemary or sage for a delicious herby flavour.

Thai beef mussaman

Make this delicious one pot your new Friday night treat. It goes really well with the Stir-fry Veggies on page 119.

ProPoints values per serving	
ProPoints values per recipe	46
Serves 4	

 20 minutes preparation
18 minutes cooking

calorie controlled cooking spray

500 g (1 lb 2 oz) lean fillet steak**, cut into thin strips**

45 g (1½ oz) red Thai curry paste

400 g (14 oz) waxy potatoes**, such as Desirée, peeled and cut into even chunks**

300 ml (10 fl oz) beef or vegetable stock

400 ml can reduced fat coconut milk

1 red pepper**, de-seeded and cut into strips**

150 g (5½ oz) frozen peas

salt and freshly ground black pepper

1 Heat a wide saucepan over a high heat and spray with the cooking spray. Cook the beef strips and curry paste for 1–2 minutes, in batches, stirring until lightly browned. Remove and set aside on a plate.

2 Add the potatoes, stock and coconut milk to the saucepan and bring to the boil. Lower the heat and simmer for 15 minutes until almost tender. Add the red pepper and cook for a further 3 minutes.

3 Return the beef to the pan and add the peas. Bring to a simmer and cook for a further 3 minutes until the peas are cooked. Season and serve immediately.

Freezing

At the end of step 3, divide equally between foil trays or containers. Leave to go cold. Seal, label and freeze for up to 3 months.

Serving

Defrost and reheat on a low heat for 5–7 minutes until piping hot, stirring occasionally. Alternatively, microwave on high for 4 minutes, stirring halfway through. Leave to stand for 1 minute before serving.

Roasted pepper lamb pasta

This works well with any type of pasta, such as shells, penne or rigatoni.

ProPoints values per serving	
ProPoints values per recipe	43
Serves 4	

 25 minutes preparation
25 minutes cooking

calorie controlled cooking spray

400 g (14 oz) lean lamb mince

1 onion, chopped finely

1 garlic clove, crushed

200 g (7 oz) dried wholewheat pasta,
   such as fusilli

1 tablespoon dried oregano

½ teaspoon dried mint

2 × 150 g portions Ultimate Tomato
   Sauce (page 120), defrosted (or see
   Cook's tip)

150 g (5½ oz) roasted red peppers from a
   jar, drained and diced

50 g (1¾ oz) low fat soft cheese

salt and freshly ground black pepper

finely chopped parsley, to garnish
   (optional)

1 Heat a wide lidded non-stick saucepan over a high heat and spray with the cooking spray. Cook the lamb mince, onion and garlic for 5 minutes until browned all over, stirring often.

2 Meanwhile, bring a saucepan of water to the boil. Add the wholewheat pasta and cook for 10–12 minutes, or according to the packet instructions, then drain.

3 Add the oregano, mint and Ultimate Tomato Sauce to the mince, cover and simmer for 20 minutes. Stir in the peppers and soft cheese and simmer for 5 minutes. Season generously, mix in the cooked pasta and serve in bowls, garnished with finely chopped parsley, if liked.

Freezing

At the end of step 3, divide equally between foil trays or containers. Leave to go cold. Seal, label and freeze for up to 3 months.

Serving

Defrost and reheat on a low heat for 5–7 minutes until piping hot, stirring occasionally. Alternatively, microwave on high for 4 minutes, stirring halfway through. Leave to stand for 1 minute before serving.

Cook's tips If you don't have any Ultimate Tomato Sauce already made, you can replace it with 300 g (10½ oz) passata.

Pepperdew peppers work brilliantly in place of the roasted red peppers from a jar – they'll add an extra zing of flavour.

Chorizo and soya bean risotto

You could use peas instead of the soya beans, for 10 **ProPoints** values per serving.

ProPoints values per serving	**11** ProPoints value
ProPoints values per recipe	**46**
Serves 4	

 45 minutes in total

150 g (5½ oz) frozen soya beans

a kettleful of boiling water

calorie controlled cooking spray

100 g (3½ oz) chorizo, cut into small cubes

500 ml (18 fl oz) hot vegetable stock

1 onion**, chopped**

2 garlic cloves**, crushed**

250 g (9 oz) dried Arborio risotto rice

125 ml (4 fl oz) dry white wine (or see Cook's tip)

1 courgette**, trimmed and grated**

zest of ½ lemon

25 g (1 oz) freshly grated Parmesan cheese

salt and freshly ground black pepper

1 Put the soya beans in a small pan and cover with boiling water. Cook at a simmer for 3 minutes, then drain and set aside. Heat a large lidded saucepan to a medium heat and spray with the cooking spray. Cook the chorizo pieces for 5 minutes until lightly browned all over. Remove with a slotted spoon and set aside to drain on kitchen towel.

2 Put a small lidded saucepan on the hob, pour in the stock, cover and keep hot (barely simmering) on a low heat while you make the risotto.

3 Spray the pan in which you cooked the chorizo with the cooking spray and cook the onion and garlic gently, covered, for 5 minutes, stirring occasionally. Add the rice and cook for 1 minute, stirring, until the rice starts to look slightly translucent. Add the wine to the pan and bubble until it is absorbed.

4 Add a third of the hot stock to the rice pan and simmer gently until all the liquid has been absorbed, stirring occasionally. Repeat with the stock twice more until the rice is swollen, slightly sticky and tender, but still has a little bit of bite left to it. If the rice still seems too firm, add a little boiling water and cook for a couple of minutes more.

5 Stir the beans, chorizo, courgette, lemon zest and Parmesan cheese into the risotto, cover with a lid and set aside for 5 minutes. Check the seasoning and serve immediately.

Freezing

At the end of step 5, divide equally between foil trays or containers and leave to go cold. Seal, label and freeze for up to 3 months.

Serving

Defrost and warm in a pan with a splash of boiling water until piping hot.

Cook's tip If you'd rather not use wine you could use the same amount of vegetable stock instead for 10 *ProPoints* values per serving.

Vegetarian variation Instead of chorizo, you can use 100 g (3½ oz) low fat vegetarian sausages, cut into small cubes and tossed in 1 teaspoon of smoked paprika, for 10 *ProPoints* values per serving.

Sticky glazed pork kebabs

Get ahead for the summer by marinating the pork and keeping it in the freezer, then when the sun shines you'll be ready to barbecue. Or simply enjoy all year round and cook under the grill.

ProPoints values per kebab	
ProPoints values per recipe	27
Makes 8 kebabs	

 30 minutes in total
+ 6 hours marinating

3 tablespoons tomato ketchup
2 tablespoons sweet chilli sauce
2 tablespoons soy sauce
2 tablespoons teriyaki sauce
500 g (1 lb 2 oz) lean pork loin steaks, cut into small chunks

1 Preheat the grill to medium hot. In a bowl, mix together the ketchup, chilli sauce, soy sauce and teriyaki sauce. Add the chunks of pork and stir to coat. Set aside for up to 6 hours in the fridge.

2 Thread the pork on to eight metal or wooden skewers (see Cook's tip). Line a grill tray with foil and put the pork kebabs on it. Discard the remaining marinade.

3 Cook the pork kebabs under the grill for 6–7 minutes, turning, until they are cooked through and starting to char. Set aside for 5 minutes, covered with foil, then serve.

Freezing

At the end of step 1, divide the pork equally between freezer bags or containers. Seal, label and freeze for up to 3 months.

Serving

Defrost the pork and cook from step 2.

Cook's tip If using wooden skewers, they will need to be soaked in water for 30 minutes before using, or wrap the exposed ends in foil before grilling.

Serving suggestion Serve with cooked brown basmati rice with chopped fresh coriander stirred through for an additional 5 *ProPoints* values per serving.

Herby toad in the hole

This foolproof recipe is perfect for when you've nothing in – just whip it out of the freezer and put it straight into the oven.

ProPoints values per serving	
ProPoints values per recipe	33
Serves 4	

20 minutes preparation
25 minutes cooking

calorie controlled cooking spray
8 × 37 g (1½ oz) Weight Watchers
    Premium Pork Sausages
125 g (4½ oz) plain flour
3 eggs
300 ml (10 fl oz) skimmed milk
1 tablespoon finely chopped fresh sage
    leaves
1 sprig finely chopped fresh rosemary
    leaves
2 teaspoons Dijon mustard
salt and freshly ground black pepper

1 Preheat the oven to Gas Mark 7/220°C/fan oven 200°C. Spray a medium roasting tin with the cooking spray and add the sausages. Cook in the oven for 10 minutes or until starting to brown.

2 Meanwhile, put the flour in a large bowl and make a well in the centre. Break the eggs into the well then, using an electric whisk or hand whisk, gradually whisk the eggs into the flour. Continue to whisk and gradually pour in the milk to make a smooth batter. Season and stir in the sage, rosemary and mustard. Transfer to a jug and set aside.

3 Remove the roasting tin from the oven and quickly but carefully pour the batter around the sausages. Return the tin to the oven and bake for 20–25 minutes until golden, puffed up and cooked through.

Freezing

Make the batter in step 2 and pour into a freezer and ovenproof dish that has been sprayed with the cooking spray. Add the uncooked sausages and wrap the dish with foil. Seal, label and freeze for up to 3 months.

Serving

Cook from frozen in a preheated oven at Gas Mark 7/220°C/fan oven 200°C for 30–40 minutes until golden and piping hot.

Serving suggestion Serve with gravy made from 2 teaspoons of gravy granules per person for an extra 1 *ProPoints* value per serving.

Parma ham and pesto pizza

Few things beat home-made pizza and this Italian classic is delicious, with its thin and crispy base. It's perfect to pull out of the freezer on a Friday night and pop straight into the oven.

ProPoints values per ½ pizza

ProPoints values per recipe	**39**
Makes 2 pizzas	

 25 minutes preparation + 20 minutes proving; 18 minutes cooking

200 g (7 oz) plain flour
½ × 7 g sachet dried fast action yeast
50 g (1¾ oz) ready-made pesto sauce
½ red onion, sliced finely
8 × 17 g slices Parma ham
50 g (1¾ oz) roasted red peppers in brine, drained and sliced
125 g pack reduced fat mozzarella, sliced
1 tablespoon dried oregano
salt and freshly ground black pepper

1 Put the flour, yeast and a pinch of salt in a bowl and gradually mix in 200 ml (7 fl oz) of tepid water until the mixture forms a soft dough. Knead for 5 minutes on a large piece of non-stick baking parchment then put back in the bowl, cover with cling film and leave to prove for 20 minutes.

2 Preheat the oven to Gas Mark 7/220°C/fan oven 200°C and put two baking trays in the oven to heat. Punch down the dough to knock it back and then divide in half. Roll one half of dough on the baking paper until it is a circle about 28 cm (11 inches) in diameter. Spread the circle with half the pesto, leaving a 1 cm (½ inch) border. Then scatter over half the onion, crumple over half the Parma ham and dot around half the peppers and mozzarella. Sprinkle with half the oregano and season with black pepper. Repeat with the remaining dough and ingredients.

3 Remove the baking trays from the oven, slide each pizza on its baking parchment on to a tray and bake in the oven for 15–18 minutes until lightly golden. Cut the pizzas in half and serve immediately.

Freezing

At the end of step 2, open freeze the pizzas on baking trays for 4–6 hours until frozen. Then wrap in baking parchment and foil. Seal, label and freeze for up to 3 months.

Serving

Unwrap the pizzas, put on baking parchment and cook from frozen as in step 3 for 18–20 minutes, until golden and piping hot.

Variation Replace the Parma ham with 125 g (4½ oz) sliced pepperoni instead for 11 *ProPoints* values per half pizza.

Cook's tip You could also use 4 x 25 ml (1 fl oz) defrosted cubes of frozen Parsley Pesto Sauce (page 120) instead of the ready-made pesto sauce for 10 *ProPoints* values per half pizza.

"The bake-in-the-oven bags that I buy from the fishmonger or cookshop are so convenient and easy to use."

Rachel McKenzie Weight Watchers member

Fish + Seafood

Hot and peppery fish cakes

Impress everyone with these amazing fish cakes. Serve with a mixed salad or a portion of the French Fries on page 104, grilled tomato halves, 75 g (2¾ oz) cooked peas and 1 tablespoon soured cream per person for 5 extra **ProPoints** values per serving.

ProPoints values per fish cake	
ProPoints values per recipe	**40**
Makes 8 fish cakes	

 15 minutes preparation
45 minutes cooking

**400 g (14 oz) floury potatoes, such as
    King Edward or Maris Piper, peeled
    and cut into even size chunks**
**350 g (12 oz) smoked peppered
    mackerel fillets, skin discarded and
    flesh flaked**
zest of 1 small lemon
1 egg, beaten
1 tablespoon horseradish sauce
50 g (1¾ oz) wild rocket, chopped
calorie controlled cooking spray
salt and freshly ground black pepper

1 Preheat the oven to Gas Mark 6/200°C/fan oven 180°C. Put the potatoes in a saucepan and cover with water. Bring to the boil, then reduce the heat and simmer for 20–25 minutes until tender. Drain thoroughly and leave to steam dry for 5 minutes. Return to the pan and mash with a fork until roughly mashed. Leave to go cold.

2 Put the potato in a bowl and mix with the mackerel, lemon zest, egg, horseradish sauce and rocket. Season generously and then, using wet hands, shape into eight fish cakes.

3 Spray a non-stick baking tray with the cooking spray and put the fish cakes on it. Spray the fish cakes again and bake in the oven for 15–18 minutes until golden and cooked through, then serve.

Freezing

At the end of step 2, layer the fish cakes between baking paper in a freezerproof container. Seal, label and freeze for up to 3 months.

Serving

Defrost thoroughly and then cook as per step 3 until golden and cooked through.

Salmon en croûte

This is so simple to make and, best of all, it can be made and frozen in advance. Serve with 100 g (3½ oz) new potatoes per person, tossed in a little chopped fresh dill, and a generous Italian-style salad with leaves, tomatoes, radish and cucumber dressed with fat-free dressing for 2 extra **ProPoints** values per serving.

ProPoints values per serving	
ProPoints values per recipe	**60**
Serves 6	

35 minutes preparation
40 minutes cooking

calorie controlled cooking spray
1 onion, chopped finely
150 g (5½ oz) mushrooms, chopped finely
1 garlic clove, crushed
140 g bag watercress, rocket and spinach, chopped roughly
zest of ½ lemon
150 g (5½ oz) low fat soft cheese
1 tablespoon chopped fresh dill
1 tablespoon chopped fresh chives
5 × 45 g (1½ oz) sheets filo pastry, measuring 50 cm × 24 cm (20 × 9½ inches)
40 g (1½ oz) dried breadcrumbs
6 × 130 g (5 oz) skinless salmon fillets
salt and freshly ground black pepper

1 Preheat the oven to Gas Mark 6/200°C/fan oven 180°C. Heat a wide, lidded non-stick saucepan and spray with the cooking spray. Cook the onion and mushrooms, covered, over a medium heat for 10 minutes. Add the garlic and cook for 1 minute. Stir in the watercress, rocket and spinach and heat through until wilted. Increase the heat briefly to allow any water to evaporate. Transfer to a bowl and leave to go cold.

2 Stir the lemon zest, soft cheese, dill and chives into the watercress mixture and season. Put a sheet of filo pastry on a large piece of baking parchment and spray with the cooking spray. Stack another two sheets on top, spraying with the cooking spray between each layer.

3 Sprinkle the breadcrumbs over the pastry in a wide line along the centre, leaving a 10 cm (4 inch) gap at either end. Sit the salmon fillets in a row along the breadcrumbs, side by side. Spread the watercress mixture over the top of the salmon fillets.

4 Spray the exposed pastry with the cooking spray, and also spray the remaining two sheets. Fold up the ends and sides of the pastry to enclose the salmon. It will still be open on the top. Crumple up the remaining two sheets of pastry and arrange them on the top of the salmon where it is still exposed.

5 Transfer the salmon to a non-stick baking tray, using the baking parchment to lift it, and cook for 35–40 minutes until golden and cooked through. Serve immediately, cut into slices.

Freezing

At the end of step 4, wrap carefully in cling film and then foil. Seal, label and freeze for up to 3 months.

Serving

Defrost and cook as per step 5 until piping hot.

Baked scampi

These delicious chip shop favourites can be cooked straight from frozen and taste great served with a portion of the French Fries on page 104, 75 g (2¾ oz) mashed peas, 1 tablespoon tartare sauce and lemon wedges per person for an extra 6 **ProPoints** values per serving.

ProPoints values per serving	4
ProPoints values per recipe	25
Serves 6	

20 minutes preparation
10 minutes cooking

calorie controlled cooking spray
200 g (7 oz) fresh breadcrumbs
2 tablespoons sesame seeds
zest of 1 lemon
1 tablespoon plain flour
1 egg, beaten
400 g (14 oz) peeled raw tiger prawns
salt and freshly ground black pepper

1 Preheat the oven to Gas Mark 7/220°C/fan oven 200°C. Heat a non-stick frying pan over a medium heat and spray with the cooking spray. Cook the breadcrumbs and sesame seeds for 5 minutes until lightly golden, stirring occasionally. Transfer to a bowl and mix with the lemon zest and some seasoning. Whizz with a hand-held blender, or alternatively, transfer to a food processor and whizz until fine crumbs are formed. Leave to go cold.

2 Put the flour in a bowl and the egg in another bowl. Dip the prawns in the flour, then the egg and then the breadcrumbs, one at a time, tossing until coated.

3 Spray a non-stick baking tray with the cooking spray and put the prawns on the tray in a single layer. Spray again with the cooking spray and bake in the oven for 8–10 minutes until golden and cooked. Serve immediately.

Freezing

At the end of step 2, open freeze the prawns on a baking tray for 4–6 hours until frozen, then divide into freezer bags. Seal, label and freeze for up to 3 months.

Serving

Cook from frozen in a preheated oven, Gas Mark 7/220°C/fan oven 200°C for 10 minutes until golden and cooked through.

Peperonata cod

This great freezer stand-by is ideal served with 100 g (3½ oz) sliced cooked new potatoes per person and some tenderstem broccoli, for an extra 2 **ProPoints** values per serving.

4 ProPoints value

ProPoints values per serving	
ProPoints values per recipe	**17**
Serves 4	

15 minutes preparation
20 minutes cooking

calorie controlled cooking spray
1 red onion**, sliced**
1 red pepper**, de-seeded and diced**
2 garlic cloves**, crushed**
1 tablespoon small capers, rinsed
2 tablespoons chopped fresh flat leaf parsley
600 g jar passata
2 teaspoons caster sugar
50 g (1¾ oz) stoned black olives in brine, drained
4 × 150 g (5½ oz) fresh skinless cod loin fillets **(not previously frozen)**
50 g (1¾ oz) dried or fresh breadcrumbs
salt and freshly ground black pepper

1 Preheat the oven to Gas Mark 5/190°C/fan oven 170°C. Heat a lidded non-stick saucepan over a medium heat and spray with the cooking spray. Cook the onion and pepper for 5 minutes, covered, until starting to soften, then stir in the garlic and cook for 1 minute. Stir in the capers, parsley, passata, sugar and olives and bring to the boil. Season.

2 Put the cod loin fillets in a 1 litre (1¾ pint) freezerproof and ovenproof dish. Pour over the tomato sauce to cover the fish and then sprinkle with the breadcrumbs.

3 Spray the top with the cooking spray and bake in the oven for 20 minutes, until the fish is cooked through. Serve immediately.

Freezing

At the end of step 1, leave the sauce to go cold, then prepare as in step 2. Wrap, seal, label and freeze for up to 3 months.

Serving

Defrost and cook as per step 3 until piping hot.

Variation **Replace the cod with** haddock loins **for the same ProPoints values per serving.**

Prawn pepper tartlets

These lovely tartlets are so easy to make – and perfect for when you want to eat quickly yet save some for another time.

ProPoints values per tartlet **9**

ProPoints values per recipe **36**
Makes 4 tartlets

15 minutes preparation + cooling
25 minutes cooking

250 g (9 oz) ready-made puff pastry
calorie controlled cooking spray
50 g (1¾ oz) roasted red peppers from a
    jar, drained and diced
1 tablespoon tomato purée
a pinch of cayenne pepper
100 g (3½ oz) low fat soft cheese
400 g (14 oz) peeled raw tiger prawns
1 tablespoon chopped fresh flat leaf
    parsley
salt and freshly ground black pepper

1 Preheat the oven to Gas Mark 5/190°C/fan oven 170°C. On a piece of baking parchment, roll out the pastry until it is about 30 × 18 cm (12 × 7 inches). Cut into four even pieces. You may wish to trim the edges of the pastry first to make it more of a rectangle.

2 Lightly score a 1 cm (½ inch) border around the edge of each pastry rectangle. Prick the inside pastry all over with a fork, spray with the cooking spray and bake in the oven for 15 minutes until golden and risen. Once out of the oven, push down the raised middle of each pastry with the back of a spoon and allow to cool.

3 In a bowl, mix together half of the peppers, the tomato purée, cayenne pepper and soft cheese. Season and then divide equally between the cases, spreading with a teaspoon. In another bowl, mix together the remaining peppers, the prawns and parsley. Top each pastry case with a quarter of the prawn mixture.

4 Bake in the oven for 10 minutes until the prawns are cooked through. Serve immediately or serve cold.

Freezing

At the end of step 3, leave to go cold, then arrange the tartlets in a freezerproof container, layered with greaseproof paper. Seal, label and freeze for up to 3 months.

Serving

Defrost and cook as per step 4 until piping hot.

Salmon and couscous parcels

Ideal for freezing, these foil wrapped parcels are great for taking out of the freezer in the morning, allowing to defrost during the day and popping in the oven for just 15 minutes in the evening – an instant dinner.

ProPoints values per serving	13 ProPoints value
ProPoints values per recipe	**51**
Serves 4	

15 minutes preparation
15 minutes cooking

15 g (½ oz) **pine nuts**

200 g (7 oz) **dried couscous**

300 ml (10 fl oz) **boiling hot vegetable stock**

25 g (1 oz) **dried unsweetened cranberries**

2 tablespoons **chopped** fresh mint

2 tablespoons **chopped** fresh basil

½ teaspoon **ground mixed spice**

4 × 130 g (5 oz) **skinless** salmon fillets

4 tablespoons **white wine**

salt and freshly ground black pepper

1 Preheat the oven to Gas Mark 5/190°C/fan oven 170°C. To toast the pine nuts, put a dry frying pan on a medium heat, add the pine nuts and cook for 1–2 minutes, stirring, until toasted and golden. Remove and cool. Put the couscous in a bowl and cover with the vegetable stock. Cover with cling film and set aside for 10 minutes.

2 Lay four large squares of foil on a work surface. Mix the cranberries, pine nuts, mint, basil, mixed spice and some seasoning into the couscous, then put a quarter of the couscous into the centre of each foil square.

3 Top each couscous mound with a salmon fillet and drizzle each with 1 tablespoon of the white wine. Fold up the corners of the foil and seal it to make a parcel.

4 Put the parcels on a baking tray and bake in the oven for 15 minutes until cooked. Serve immediately.

Freezing

At the end of step 1, make sure the couscous is cold. Then prepare as per the recipe to the end of step 3. Wrap, seal and place in a freezerproof container then label and freeze for up to 3 months.

Serving

Defrost and cook as per step 4.

Smoked haddock and sweet potato gratin

The smoked haddock gives a really rich flavour to this tasty take on a classic fish pie.

ProPoints values per serving	**9** ProPoints value
ProPoints values per recipe	37
Serves 4	

35 minutes preparation
25 minutes cooking

1 head of broccoli**, chopped into small**
    florets
400 g (14 oz) sweet potato**, peeled and**
    cut into thin slices
125 ml (4 fl oz) dry white wine
200 g (7 oz) low fat soft cheese
300 ml (10 fl oz) fish stock
2 teaspoons cornflour mixed with
    1 tablespoon water
400 g (14 oz) skinless smoked haddock**,**
    cut into chunks
198 g can sweetcorn**, drained**
calorie controlled cooking spray
salt and freshly ground black pepper

1 Preheat the oven to Gas Mark 4/180°C/fan oven 160°C. Bring a large pan of water to the boil and add the broccoli. Cook for 5 minutes. Remove with a slotted spoon and set aside. Add the sweet potato to the water and simmer for 10 minutes until tender. Drain thoroughly and set aside.

2 Put the white wine in a medium pan and bring to the boil. Bubble for 3–5 minutes until reduced by half and then stir in the soft cheese, fish stock and cornflour mixture. Bring to the boil and cook for 1 minute, then season.

3 Put the haddock, broccoli and sweetcorn in the base of a 1 litre (1¾ pint) ovenproof dish. Pour over the white wine sauce and arrange the potato slices on top.

4 Spray the top with the cooking spray and bake in the oven for 20–25 minutes until lightly golden and cooked through.

Freezing

Leave all the vegetables and sauce to go cold. Then assemble as in step 3, spooning and spreading the sauce if it has thickened. Wrap, seal, label and freeze for up to 3 months.

Serving

Defrost and cook as per step 4 until piping hot.

Seafood linguine

Use the Parsley Pesto Sauce on page 120 as a base for this easy creamy pasta dish.

ProPoints values per serving	**9** ProPoints value
ProPoints values per recipe	**38**
Serves 4	

 30 minutes in total

200 g (7 oz) dried linguine
200 g tub low fat soft cheese
4 × 25 ml (1 fl oz) portions frozen Parsley
 Pesto Sauce (page 120), defrosted
1 tablespoon chopped fresh dill
zest of ½ lemon
400 g (14 oz) frozen cooked seafood **mix**
salt and freshly ground black pepper

1 Bring a large lidded saucepan of water to the boil and cook the pasta for 10–12 minutes, or according to the packet instructions, until al dente. Reserve 100 ml (3½ fl oz) of the cooking liquid. Drain the pasta in a colander and leave to steam dry for 5 minutes.

2 Put the soft cheese, pesto sauce, dill, lemon zest and some seasoning in the empty pasta pan. Gradually add the reserved pasta cooking water and gently heat until smooth. Add the seafood and gently simmer, covered, for 5 minutes, until the seafood is defrosted and heated through. Stir through the pasta and serve.

Freezing

At the end of step 1, rinse the pasta in cold water and drain thoroughly, then divide equally between foil trays or containers. At the end of step 2, leave the sauce – minus the seafood – to go cold and divide equally between the foil trays or containers, on top of the pasta. Be sure to keep the seafood frozen. Seal, label and freeze for up to 3 months.

Serving

Defrost the sauce and the seafood and cook in a pan as per step 2, cooking until piping hot. You may need to add a splash of water.

Cook's tip **Replace the Parsley Pesto Sauce with 50 g (1¾ oz) ready-made reduced fat pesto, for 10 *ProPoints* values per serving.**

"When you're grating cheese, always use the small side of the grater and that way you feel like you are having lots of cheese!"

Narelle Halford Weight Watchers member

Vegetarian

The nicest sweet potato and goat's cheese rösti

You don't need much goat's cheese to make these slightly sweet rösti wonderfully tangy, which means the **ProPoints** values stay low. Serve with a salad, such as chopped tomato and watercress.

ProPoints values per 2 rösti	
ProPoints values per recipe	**40**
Makes 12 rösti	

20 minutes preparation
25 minutes cooking

750 g (1 lb 10 oz) sweet potatoes, **peeled and grated coarsely**

calorie controlled cooking spray

1 red onion, **diced finely**

1 garlic clove, **crushed**

200 g (7 oz) hard goat's cheese, crumbled

3 tablespoons chopped fresh coriander

2 eggs, **beaten**

salt and freshly ground black pepper

1 Preheat the oven to Gas Mark 6/200°C/fan oven 180°C. Put the grated sweet potato in a clean tea towel and squeeze out any liquid. Then put the sweet potato in a large bowl.

2 Heat a non-stick frying pan over a medium heat and spray with the cooking spray. Cook the onion and garlic for 3–4 minutes until softened. Add them to the grated potato, along with the cheese, coriander and eggs. Season and then form into 12 rough cakes, squeezing to shape.

3 Spray a non-stick baking tray with the cooking spray and put the rösti on the tray. Spray with the cooking spray and bake in the oven for 20–25 minutes until golden brown and cooked through. Serve immediately.

Freezing

At the end of step 2, layer the rösti between baking parchment in a freezerproof container. Seal, label and freeze for up to 3 months.

Serving

Defrost the röstis then cook as per step 3 until golden and crispy.

Cook's tip You can freeze any leftover hard goat's cheese for up to 3 months. Just defrost and use next time.

Twice-baked cheese soufflés

Since these soufflés are cooked twice, there is no danger of them deflating like the classic soufflé. Serve with tenderstem broccoli and 100 g (3½ oz) sliced new potatoes per person for an extra 2 **ProPoints** values per serving.

ProPoints values per soufflé	
ProPoints values per recipe	**45**
Makes 8 soufflés	

 15 minutes preparation + 10 minutes cooling; 32 minutes cooking

60 g (2 oz) low fat soft spread
125 g (4½ oz) plain flour
425 ml (15 fl oz) skimmed milk
4 eggs, **separated**
1 heaped teaspoon English mustard
1 teaspoon lemon zest
1 tablespoon fresh thyme **leaves**
75 g (2¾ oz) hard goat's cheese, grated
75 g (2¾ oz) reduced fat mature Cheddar cheese, grated
a kettleful of boiling water
75 g (2¾ oz) Weight Watchers West Country Thick Cream
salt and freshly ground black pepper

1 Preheat the oven to Gas Mark 4/180°C/fan oven 160°C. Use 1 teaspoon of the low fat spread to grease eight 150 ml (5 fl oz) pudding basins or ramekins and line the bases with baking parchment. Put the remaining low fat spread in a saucepan and melt over a low heat. Stir in the flour then remove from the heat and gradually add the milk, whisking until smooth. Return the mixture to the heat and bubble for 1 minute until thick.

2 Remove the mixture from the heat and stir in the egg yolks, mustard, lemon zest, thyme, goat's cheese, half the Cheddar cheese and some seasoning. In a clean, grease-free bowl, whisk the egg whites until they form soft peaks, then fold them into the cheese mixture, using a metal spoon. Spoon all the mixture into the ramekins.

3 Put the ramekins in a roasting tin and then pour boiling water into the tin until it reaches halfway up the ramekins. Bake in the oven for 15–20 minutes until risen. Run a knife around the edges and leave to cool for 10 minutes.

4 To serve, raise the oven temperature to Gas Mark 7/220°C/fan oven 200°C. Remove the soufflés from their dishes, discard the paper and transfer to a shallow ovenproof dish. Sprinkle with the remaining Cheddar cheese and spoon a little cream over each. Bake in the oven for 10–12 minutes until puffed up and golden. Serve immediately.

Freezing

At the end of step 3, leave to go cold, remove from the ramekins and transfer to a freezerproof container. Seal, label and freeze for up to 3 months.

Serving

Defrost and cook as per step 4 until piping hot.

Cook's tip **If you're not a fan of goat's cheese, then just use all reduced fat mature Cheddar cheese. The ProPoints values will be 5 per serving.**

Butternut squash and coconut curry

This curry's great for when you want to freeze your leftovers as it makes enough for 6 servings – have what you need for dinner and freeze the rest for another time. Serve with 60 g (2 oz) dried basmati rice per person, cooked until tender, and with lime wedges on the side for an extra 6 **ProPoints** values per serving.

ProPoints values per serving	
ProPoints values per recipe	23
Serves 6	

 20 minutes preparation
1 hour cooking

1.25 kg (2 lb 12 oz) butternut squash,
   peeled, de-seeded and cut into cubes
calorie controlled cooking spray
1 teaspoon cumin seeds
1 large onion, chopped
2.5 cm (1 inch) fresh root ginger, peeled
   and diced
1 red chilli, de-seeded and sliced
2 teaspoons garam masala
400 ml (14 fl oz) vegetable stock
200 ml (7 fl oz) fresh pineapple juice
400 ml can reduced fat coconut milk
100 g (3½ oz) low fat soft cheese
225 g can water chestnuts, drained
100 g bag baby spinach
25 g (1 oz) roasted cashew nuts, chopped
salt and freshly ground black pepper

1 Preheat the oven to Gas Mark 6/200°C/fan oven 180°C. Put the squash on a non-stick baking tray and spray with the cooking spray. Sprinkle with the cumin seeds and lightly toss. Bake in the oven for 45–60 minutes until roasted and tender.

2 Meanwhile, heat a wide non-stick saucepan over a medium heat and spray with the cooking spray. Cook the onion, ginger and chilli for 5 minutes until softened. Then add the garam masala and cook for 30 seconds. Add the vegetable stock, pineapple juice and coconut milk and bring to the boil, then lower the heat and simmer for 10 minutes until it has reduced a little. Stir in the soft cheese until smooth.

3 When the squash is cooked, add it to the curry along with the water chestnuts and spinach. Stir until the curry has heated through and the spinach has wilted. Check the seasoning and serve, sprinkled with the cashew nuts.

Freezing

At the end of step 3, divide equally between foil trays or containers then leave to go cold. Seal, label and freeze for up to 3 months.

Serving

Defrost and reheat in a pan until piping hot.

Caramelised onion and Gorgonzola tart

Serve with watercress drizzled with a little balsamic vinegar and 100 g (3½ oz) sliced, boiled new potatoes per person for 2 extra **ProPoints** values per serving.

ProPoints values per serving	
ProPoints values per recipe	**41**
Serves 4	

20 minutes preparation
50 minutes cooking

calorie controlled cooking spray
275 g (9½ oz) onions**, sliced thinly**
2 teaspoons soft brown sugar
1 garlic clove**, crushed**
1 tablespoon fresh thyme **leaves**
250 g (9 oz) plain flour
100 g (3½ oz) low fat spread
3 tablespoons skimmed milk
50 g (1¾ oz) Gorgonzola cheese, crumbled
salt and freshly ground black pepper

1 Preheat the oven to Gas Mark 4/180°C/fan oven 160°C. Heat a wide, lidded non-stick saucepan and spray with the cooking spray. Cook the onions on a low heat for 20 minutes, covered, stirring occasionally, until softened and golden. Add the brown sugar and heat for a few minutes until dissolved, then increase the heat and cook for 5 minutes until the onions have caramelised. Stir in the garlic and thyme leaves and season.

2 Meanwhile, put the flour in a bowl and rub in the low fat spread with your fingertips until it resembles breadcrumbs. Add the skimmed milk and stir until it comes together. Roll out into a large rectangle, about 28 × 23 cm (11 × 9 inches), on a piece of baking paper.

3 Spread the onions all over the tart, leaving about a 2.5 cm (1 inch) border. Scatter the Gorgonzola cheese on top, then press the fork tines into the edge.

4 Transfer to a baking sheet and bake in the oven for 20–25 minutes until lightly golden. Serve cut into squares.

Freezing

At the end of step 3, leave to go cold then wrap the tart in parchment and foil. Seal, label and freeze for up to 3 months.

Serving

Defrost and cook as per step 4 until piping hot.

Italian pasta bake

Like a lasagne but without the layers, this delicious bake can be cooked directly from frozen, so is great for when you've arrived home and realised the cupboards are empty! Serve with a generous side salad of rocket, spinach and watercress with roasted cherry tomatoes for no extra **ProPoints** values.

ProPoints values per serving	
ProPoints values per recipe	**45**
Serves 4	

30 minutes preparation
40 minutes cooking

calorie controlled cooking spray
1 red onion, chopped
1 red pepper, de-seeded and diced finely
350 g pack Quorn mince
2 tablespoons dried mixed herbs
2 tablespoons sun-dried tomato purée
300 ml (10 fl oz) vegetable stock
400 g can chopped tomatoes
200 g (7 oz) dried pasta shells
250 g tub quark
200 g (7 oz) low fat soft cheese
**35 g (1¼ oz) slice wholemeal bread,
    grated coarsely**
1 garlic clove, crushed
2 tablespoons fresh flat leaf parsley
salt and freshly ground black pepper

1 Preheat the oven to Gas Mark 4/180°C/fan oven 160°C. Heat a wide non-stick saucepan over a medium heat and spray with the cooking spray. Cook the onion, red pepper and Quorn mince for 5 minutes, stirring occasionally, until softened and just starting to brown.

2 Add the mixed herbs and tomato purée and cook for 1 minute. Stir in the vegetable stock and tomatoes and cook gently for 10 minutes. Season generously.

3 Meanwhile, bring a pan of water to the boil and cook the pasta for 6 minutes only (it will finish cooking in the oven), then drain thoroughly. Mix the pasta into the Quorn sauce and then transfer to a 1 litre (1¾ pint) ovenproof dish.

4 In a bowl, mix together the quark and soft cheese. Spread this over the pasta and Quorn mince to cover the top. Mix together the breadcrumbs with the garlic and parsley and scatter over the top.

5 Spray the top with the cooking spray and bake in the oven for 30–40 minutes until golden and bubbling, then serve.

Freezing

At the end of step 4, leave to go cold. Wrap in foil, label and freeze for up to 3 months.

Serving

Spray the top with the cooking spray and cook from frozen in a preheated oven, Gas Mark 4/180°C/fan oven 160°C for 40–50 minutes, until piping hot and golden.

Aubergine cannelloni

The secret is to cut the aubergine into small cubes and cook them until soft and tender. Serve each portion with a generous baby leaf and tomato salad dressed with fat free dressing.

ProPoints values per serving	5 ProPoints value
ProPoints values per recipe	**19**
Serves 4	

40 minutes preparation
30 minutes cooking

calorie controlled cooking spray

**2 aubergines, trimmed and cut
into 1 cm (½ inch) cubes**

2 garlic cloves, crushed

1 onion, diced finely

1 tablespoon tomato purée

500 g carton passata

1 tablespoon dried oregano

225 ml (8 fl oz) vegetable stock

1 tablespoon caster sugar

1 tablespoon red wine vinegar

a few fresh basil leaves, chopped

8 × 14 g dried cannelloni tubes

**125 g pack reduced fat mozzarella,
drained and sliced**

salt and freshly ground black pepper

1 Preheat the oven to Gas Mark 6/200°C/fan oven 180°C. Heat a wide, lidded non-stick saucepan over a medium heat and spray generously with the cooking spray. Add 3 tablespoons of water and cook the aubergine, garlic and onion on a low heat for 20 minutes, covered, until tender and cooked through. Add the tomato purée and cook for 1 minute. Season and transfer to a bowl to cool.

2 Meanwhile, put the passata, oregano, stock, sugar, vinegar and basil in a small pan and bring to the boil. Season generously and set aside.

3 Using a teaspoon, fill each cannelloni tube with some of the aubergine mixture. Pour about a third of the tomato sauce into the base of a shallow 1 litre (1¾ pint) ovenproof dish. Arrange the cannelloni tubes in a single layer in the dish. Stir any leftover aubergine mixture into the remaining tomato sauce and pour it over the cannelloni. Arrange the mozzarella on the top.

4 Bake in the oven for 25–30 minutes until the cheese is golden and bubbling and the pasta is cooked, then serve.

Freezing

To freeze the entire dish, at the end of step 2, allow the aubergines and tomato sauce to go cold. Then continue to prepare as above until the end of step 3. Wrap in foil, label and freeze for up to 3 months.

Serving

Defrost and cook as per step 4, until piping hot and golden.

Giant samosas

This version of an Indian classic is a cross between a pasty and a samosa and can be put in the oven straight from the freezer. Serve with a shredded iceberg lettuce and carrot salad as well as 2 tablespoons low fat plain yogurt mixed with 1 teaspoon mint sauce per person for an extra 1 **ProPoints** value per serving.

ProPoints values per samosa	
ProPoints values per recipe	44
Makes 4 samosas	

 1 hour preparation
30 minutes cooking

calorie controlled cooking spray
1 onion, chopped
200 g (7 oz) butternut squash, peeled, de-seeded and cut into 1 cm (½ inch) cubes
100 g (3½ oz) potatoes, peeled and cut into 1 cm (½ inch) cubes
1 red pepper, de-seeded and diced finely
40 g (1½ oz) mild curry paste
100 g bag baby spinach leaves, chopped
100 g (3½ oz) frozen peas
2 plum tomatoes, skinned, de-seeded and cut into 1 cm (½ inch) cubes
325 g (11½ oz) wholemeal flour, plus 1 tablespoon for kneading
1 tablespoon olive oil
1 egg, separated
2 tablespoons skimmed milk
1 teaspoon sesame seeds
salt and freshly ground black pepper

1 Preheat the oven to Gas Mark 5/190°C/fan oven 170°C and line a baking tray with non-stick baking parchment. Heat a wide, lidded saucepan over a medium heat and spray with the cooking spray. Cook the onion, butternut squash, potatoes and red pepper for 15 minutes, covered, until almost tender. Add the curry paste and spinach, stir thoroughly, cover, and cook for 2 minutes. Remove the lid, stir in the peas and tomatoes and season generously. Set aside until cold.

2 Meanwhile, make the pastry. In a bowl, mix together the flour, olive oil and a pinch of salt. Gradually add 175 ml (6 fl oz) cold water and mix to make a soft dough. Sprinkle the remaining 1 tablespoon of flour on the work surface and knead the dough for 5 minutes until smooth and elastic.

3 Divide the dough into four pieces. Roll a piece of dough into a large circle, about 18 cm (7 inches) in diameter, and brush the edge with a little egg white. Put a quarter of the filling mixture into the middle and fold the dough over to seal the filling. Arrange on the baking tray, seam side down. Repeat with the remaining dough and filling.

4 Score the tops of the samosas three times with a sharp knife. Mix together the egg yolk and the skimmed milk with a fork and use to brush the tops of the samosas, then sprinkle them with the sesame seeds.

5 Bake in the oven for 25–30 minutes until golden and cooked through. Serve immediately.

Freezing

At the end of step 4, open freeze the samosas on a baking tray for 4–6 hours, until frozen. Then wrap each one in cling film and put in freezer bags. Seal, label and freeze for up to 3 months.

Serving

Remove the samosas from the freezer, place on a baking tray and cook from frozen at Gas Mark 5/190°C/fan oven 170°C for 30–40 minutes, until golden, crispy and piping hot.

Home-made spinach gnocchi

A satisfying, quick Italian-inspired midweek supper the whole family will enjoy.

ProPoints values per serving	
ProPoints values per recipe	31
Serves 4	

 30 minutes in total

125 g (4½ oz) baby spinach leaves, chopped roughly

125 g (4½ oz) wild rocket, chopped roughly

a kettleful of boiling water

2 tablespoons chopped fresh flat leaf parsley leaves

1 garlic clove, crushed

150 g (5½ oz) low fat soft cheese

100 g (3½ oz) plain flour, plus 1 tablespoon for dusting

2 eggs, beaten

100 g (3½ oz) Parmesan cheese, grated

a little grated fresh nutmeg

4 × 150 g (5½ oz) portions frozen Ultimate Tomato Sauce, defrosted (page 120)

salt and freshly ground black pepper

1. Put the spinach and rocket in a large bowl and pour over enough boiling water to cover, straight from the kettle. Leave to stand for 2 minutes until wilted then drain in a colander. Press with a potato masher to squeeze out as much water as possible.

2. Dry the bowl and return the spinach and rocket. Add the parsley, garlic, soft cheese, flour, eggs, 75 g (2¾ oz) of the Parmesan cheese, the nutmeg and seasoning. Mix well until combined. Using hands dusted with flour, shape into 20 walnut-size gnocchi balls and put on a large plate.

3. Put the Ultimate Tomato Sauce in a lidded saucepan. Gently bring to the boil, reduce the heat to low, cover, and keep warm while you cook the gnocchi balls.

4. To cook the gnocchi, bring a large saucepan of water to the boil and then reduce the heat to a simmer. Cook the gnocchi in batches of six for about 3 minutes per batch, then remove with a slotted spoon and put into the tomato sauce. Repeat with the remaining balls and then serve with the remaining cheese sprinkled over.

Freezing

In step 4, place the cooked gnocchi on a plate and leave to go cold. Then open freeze on the plate or a tray, unwrapped, for 4–6 hours. Divide into freezer bags or containers. Seal, label and freeze for up to 3 months.

Serving

Defrost the Ultimate Tomato Sauce and cook the gnocchi from frozen following step 4 for 4–5 minutes until piping hot.

Spicy bean burgers

Serve each tasty burger on half a toasted 80 g (3 oz) ciabatta roll with shredded lettuce, sliced tomato and 1 tablespoon reduced fat mayonnaise per person, for an extra 4 **ProPoints** values per serving.

ProPoints values per serving	
ProPoints values per recipe	18
Serves 4	

 15 minutes preparation
15 minutes cooking

410 g can cannellini beans in water,
   drained and rinsed

410 g can butter beans in water, drained
   and rinsed

1 tablespoon medium curry powder

3 spring onions, chopped finely

1 red pepper, de-seeded and diced finely

50 g (1¾ oz) dried breadcrumbs

1 egg, beaten lightly

calorie controlled cooking spray

salt and freshly ground black pepper

1 Preheat the grill to medium and line a grill tray with foil. In a food processor or with a hand-held blender, whizz together the cannellini beans, butter beans and curry powder.

2 Transfer to a bowl, season and mix in the spring onions, red pepper, breadcrumbs and egg until combined. Divide the mixture into four equal portions and shape with wet hands into four large burgers.

3 Transfer the burgers to the grill tray and spray with the cooking spray. Grill for 12–15 minutes until golden, turning halfway through. Serve immediately.

Freezing

At the end of step 2, layer the burgers between baking paper in a freezerproof container. Seal, label and freeze for up to 3 months.

Serving

Defrost the burgers and cook as per step 3 until golden and piping hot.

Cook's tip If you have Moroccan spice mix, use this instead of the curry powder for a wonderful flavour. The *ProPoints* values remain the same.

Thai sticky rice

This fragrant stir-fry is a great midweek supper. If you like, you can add 60 g (2 oz) cooked and peeled prawns per person in step 2 for an alternative, and for an extra 2 **ProPoints** values per serving.

ProPoints values per serving	
ProPoints values per recipe	37
Serves 4	

 40 minutes in total

300 ml (10 fl oz) vegetable stock

250 g (9 oz) dried Jasmine rice, rinsed

calorie controlled cooking spray

2 eggs, beaten

1 small head of cauliflower, cut into
small florets

100 g (3½ oz) fine green beans, trimmed
and cut into short lengths

1 small onion, diced finely

2 garlic cloves, sliced

1 red chilli, de-seeded and sliced finely

150 g (5½ oz) chestnut mushrooms,
wiped, trimmed and sliced

2 tablespoons red or green Thai curry
paste

4 tablespoons soy sauce

2 tablespoons rice wine vinegar

1 tablespoon light brown soft sugar

1 tablespoon sweet chilli sauce

1 tablespoon toasted sesame oil

a handful of fresh coriander leaves

1. Put the vegetable stock in a large lidded saucepan and bring to the boil. Add the rice, stir with a fork, cover and cook on a low heat for 10 minutes. Remove from the heat and set aside with the lid on.

2. Heat a non-stick wok and spray with the cooking spray. Pour in the beaten eggs and cook for 1–2 minutes, stirring to spread the egg to make a big pancake until it just starts to set, then leave to cook briefly but don't allow it to set completely. Transfer to a clean chopping board and leave to go cold, then roll up into a sausage and shred finely.

3. Fill a saucepan a quarter full with water and bring to the boil. Add the cauliflower florets and simmer for 2 minutes, then add the beans and cook for a further 1 minute. Drain in a colander and leave to cool.

4. Heat the wok again and spray generously with the cooking spray. Add the onion, garlic, chilli and mushrooms and cook for 5 minutes, stirring until softened. Add the Thai curry paste and cook for 30 seconds, stirring.

5. Stir in the cauliflower, beans and cooked rice and stir-fry for 2 minutes. Add the soy sauce, rice wine vinegar, sugar, chilli sauce and sesame oil and stir-fry for 1–2 minutes. Scatter over the egg and coriander and serve immediately.

Freezing

At the end of step 5, leave to go cold. Divide equally between foil trays or containers. Seal, label and freeze for up to 3 months.

Serving

Defrost and stir-fry for 5–8 minutes on a high heat until hot.

"I cut butternut squash and swede into 'chips', parboil, then freeze in portions — so when everyone else wants chips I can just take them out of the freezer and bake them with some rock salt, along with everyone elses, for great zero ProPoints value 'chips'. "

Kellie Hudson Weight Watchers member

Sides + Sauces

Cheesy leeks and ham

Serve this delicious side with your Sunday roast – prep in advance then it's all ready to cook on the day.

ProPoints values per serving	5 ProPoints value
ProPoints values per recipe	19
Serves 4	

25 minutes preparation
30 minutes cooking

4 large leeks, trimmed and cut into
    10 cm (4 inch) lengths
4 × 17 g (½ oz) slices Parma ham, halved
2 tablespoons cornflour
100 g (3½ oz) reduced fat mature
    Cheddar cheese, grated
300 ml (10 fl oz) skimmed milk
½ teaspoon English mustard
25 g (1 oz) dried or fresh brown
    breadcrumbs
calorie controlled cooking spray
freshly ground black pepper

1   Preheat the oven to Gas Mark 5/190°C/fan oven 170°C. Bring a large pan of water to the boil, add the leeks, then reduce the heat and cook at a simmer for 4 minutes. Drain and rinse in cold water until cold. Dry thoroughly.

2   Wrap each piece of leek with a piece of Parma ham and arrange in a 1 litre (1¾ pint) ovenproof dish. In a small bowl, mix together the cornflour and cheese.

3   Put the milk in a small saucepan and bring just to a simmer. Add the cheese and cornflour mix and stir to melt the cheese. Bring to the boil and bubble for 1 minute until thickened. Stir in the mustard and some black pepper then pour over the leeks to cover. Sprinkle over the breadcrumbs.

4   Spray with the cooking spray and bake in the oven for 30 minutes until golden and bubbling.

Freezing

Make either in a foil tray or ovenproof dish. Allow the sauce to go cold in step 3, then spoon and spread it over the leeks and finish step 3. Wrap with foil if using the ovenproof dish. Seal, label and freeze for up to 3 months.

Serving

Defrost thoroughly and cook as per step 4 until golden and piping hot.

Cook's tip Replace the Parma ham with pancetta for 6 ProPoints values per serving.

Oven roasted rainbow veggies

Cheer up the table with these colourful vegetables, which can be cooked straight from the freezer – perfect for when you want to add something quickly to your Sunday roast.

ProPoints values per serving

ProPoints values per recipe   **8**
Serves 4

20 minutes preparation
40 minutes cooking

2 red onions, chopped roughly
800 g (1 lb 11 oz) butternut squash,
    peeled, de-seeded and cut into small
    cubes
1 red pepper, de-seeded and cut into
    chunks
1 yellow pepper, de-seeded and cut into
    chunks
1 large courgette, trimmed and cut into
    chunks
400 g (14 oz) new potatoes, halved
2 garlic cloves, sliced
2 fresh rosemary sprigs, leaves only,
    chopped
calorie controlled cooking spray
4 tablespoons balsamic vinegar
salt and freshly ground black pepper

1 Preheat the oven to Gas Mark 5/190°C/fan oven 170°C. Arrange all the vegetables in a single layer in a large roasting tin and scatter over the garlic, rosemary and seasoning. Spray with the cooking spray, toss to coat and roast in the oven for 20 minutes.

2 Stir the vegetables and drizzle over the vinegar. Continue to cook for 15–20 minutes until tender and lightly charred. Serve.

Freezing

Prepare and cook the vegetables up to the end of step 1. Remove from the oven and leave to go cold. Open freeze on a baking tray for 4–6 hours until frozen. Divide equally between 4 freezer bags or containers. Seal, label and freeze for up to 3 months.

Serving

Empty the frozen vegetables on to a roasting tray, drizzle with 1 tablespoon of the vinegar per portion and cook at Gas Mark 5/190°C/fan oven 170°C for 25–30 minutes until piping hot and lightly charred.

French fries

Few things are better than home-made oven-cooked chips – these are perfect for keeping in the freezer and adding to any meal. The recipe can easily be doubled to make eight portions in total; our photo shows two portions.

ProPoints values per serving	
ProPoints values per recipe	12
Serves 4	

20 minutes preparation
25 minutes cooking

500 g (1 lb 2 oz) **potatoes**, such as Maris
    Piper, peeled and cut into 1 cm
    (½ inch) thick chips
300 ml (10 fl oz) vegetable stock
calorie controlled cooking spray
salt and freshly ground black pepper

1 Preheat the oven to Gas Mark 7/220°C/fan oven 200°C. Put the potatoes in a wide saucepan with the vegetable stock and bring to the boil. Simmer for 5 minutes then drain in a colander.

2 Line a board with a double thickness of kitchen towel and transfer the potatoes to it. Dry the potatoes with the kitchen towel.

3 Spray a non-stick baking tray with the cooking spray and transfer the potatoes, in a single layer, on to the tray. Spray again and season. Bake in the oven for 20–25 minutes until golden and crispy, turning halfway through, then serve.

Freezing

At the end of step 2, open freeze the potatoes on a baking tray for 4–6 hours until frozen. Then divide equally between freezer bags or containers. Seal, label and freeze for up to 3 months.

Serving

Remove the potatoes from the freezer and cook as per step 3 until golden and crispy for 25–30 minutes from frozen, turning occasionally.

Cook's tip Why not sprinkle the French fries with 1 teaspoon smoked paprika or Cajun spices before baking in the oven, for no extra **ProPoints** values?

Pilau rice

This makes a perfect accompaniment to the Chicken and Aubergine Masala on page 36 and is a good side dish to keep on stand-by in the freezer.

ProPoints values per serving	**6** ProPoints value
ProPoints values per recipe	22
Serves 4	

 20 minutes preparation
15 minutes cooking

200 g (7 oz) dried basmati rice
a kettleful of boiling water
½ teaspoon cumin seeds
½ teaspoon coriander seeds
6 whole cloves
2 bay leaves
2 teaspoons ground turmeric
3 cardamom pods, split
1 cinnamon stick, split
calorie controlled cooking spray
1 onion, chopped finely
400 ml (14 fl oz) hot vegetable stock
salt and freshly ground black pepper

1 Put the rice in a large lidded saucepan, pour over boiling water to cover and bring back to the boil. Simmer for 4 minutes. Drain and rinse in cold water. Set aside.

2 Heat the saucepan again over a medium heat and add the cumin, coriander, cloves, bay leaves, turmeric, cardamom and cinnamon stick. Stir for 30 seconds until fragrant. Spray with the cooking spray and add the onion. Cook for 10 minutes on a low heat, covered, stirring occasionally, until the onion is softened.

3 Return the rice to the saucepan, stir, and pour over the stock. Bring to the boil then cover with a circle of double thickness parchment paper and a lid. Cook on a very low heat for 15 minutes until the rice is cooked. Set aside for 5 minutes. Do not lift the lid. Check the seasoning then discard the cinnamon stick and the bay leaves and serve immediately.

Freezing

Allow the rice to go cold then divide equally into portions between freezer bags or containers. Seal, label and freeze for up to 3 months.

Serving

Defrost thoroughly. Microwave one portion on high for 2 minutes and leave to stand for 1 minute before serving. Ensure the rice is piping hot. Or defrost thoroughly and put in a lidded pan with 2 tablespoons of water. Cover and reheat on a low heat for 4–5 minutes until piping hot.

Parmesan potatoes

These cheesy, garlicky, diced roasted potatoes brighten up any meal and can be cooked directly from frozen, so no need to defrost. They're fabulous with the Italian Stuffed Chicken on page 26.

***ProPoints* values per serving**	**3** ProPoints value
***ProPoints* values per recipe**	**11**
Serves 4	

20 minutes preparation
30 minutes cooking

400 g (14 oz) floury potatoes, such as Maris Piper, peeled and cut into 1 cm (½ inch) cubes

25 g (1 oz) Parmesan cheese, grated finely

1 garlic clove, crushed

calorie controlled cooking spray

salt and freshly ground black pepper

1 Preheat the oven to Gas Mark 5/190°C/fan oven 170°C and line a large baking tray with non-stick baking paper. Put the potatoes in a large pan and cover with cold water. Bring to the boil and simmer for 2 minutes. Drain in a colander and allow to sit, steam-drying, for 5 minutes.

2 In a large bowl, mix together the Parmesan cheese, garlic and seasoning. Add the potatoes and toss to coat in the cheese mix. Empty on to the baking tray, spreading in a single layer.

3 Spray the potatoes with the cooking spray and bake in the oven for 25–30 minutes, turning halfway through, until golden and crispy. Serve immediately.

Freezing

At the end of step 2, open freeze the potatoes on the baking tray for 4–6 hours until frozen. Then divide equally between freezer bags or containers. Seal, label and freeze for up to 3 months.

Serving

Remove the potatoes from the freezer and spread on a lined baking tray. Spray with the cooking spray and bake from frozen in the oven at Gas Mark 5/190°C/fan oven 170°C for 30–35 minutes, turning occasionally until golden and crispy.

Cook's tip **For plain potatoes, simply leave out the Parmesan cheese and garlic in step 2 for 2 *ProPoints* values per serving.**

Dauphinoise potatoes

Layers of scrummy potato, onion and garlic, baked until golden. These creamy spuds go well with the Must-try Pepper Crust Fillet Steak on page 42 and lots of steamed green beans.

ProPoints values per serving	**6** ProPoints value
ProPoints values per recipe	25
Serves 4	

🕐 20 minutes preparation
1 hour cooking

1 onion, **sliced finely**

2 garlic cloves, **sliced**

500 g (1 lb 2 oz) waxy potatoes, **such as Desirée, peeled and sliced thinly**

600 ml (20 fl oz) vegetable stock

150 ml (5 fl oz) light double cream alternative

25 g (1 oz) Gruyère cheese, grated

salt and freshly ground black pepper

1 Preheat the oven to Gas Mark 5/190°C/fan oven 170°C. Put the onion, garlic, potatoes and stock in a wide saucepan and bring to the boil. Lower the heat and simmer for 5 minutes. Drain the potatoes and vegetables, reserving 5 tablespoons of the stock.

2 Arrange the potatoes and onions in a 1 litre (1¾ pint) ovenproof dish. Mix the cream into the reserved stock, season and pour over the potatoes. Sprinkle over the Gruyère cheese.

3 Bake in the oven for 1 hour until golden, bubbling and tender. Serve immediately.

Freezing

At the end of step 2, leave to go cold, then seal, label and freeze for up to 3 months.

Serving

Put the frozen potatoes in a preheated oven at Gas Mark 5/190°C/fan oven 170°C for 1–1¼ hours until golden and piping hot.

Onion rings

Cook these onion rings from frozen and serve with the Spicy Bean Burgers on page 94 for a delicious treat.

ProPoints values per serving **3** ProPoints value

ProPoints values per recipe **22**
Serves 8

30 minutes preparation
25 minutes cooking

200 g (7 oz) self-raising flour
4 onions, peeled, sliced into thick
   1 cm (½ inch) rings and separated
1 egg, beaten
275 ml bottle lager
calorie controlled cooking spray
salt and freshly ground black pepper

1 Preheat the oven to Gas Mark 7/220°C/fan oven 200°C and line two large baking trays with non-stick baking parchment. Bring a wide saucepan of water to the boil. Meanwhile, put the flour in a large bowl and add the onion rings, tossing together so that the rings are coated in the flour. Remove the onion rings, shaking off the excess flour, and put on to a plate.

2 Make a well in the centre of the remaining flour and gradually stir in the egg and beer to make a thick, smooth batter. Season generously.

3 Once the water has come to the boil, lower the heat to a simmer. Use a fork to dip the onion rings into the batter to coat, then drop one at a time into the simmering water. (Don't worry – the batter doesn't come off the rings in the water.) Cook in batches of three at a time for 1 minute, then remove with a slotted spoon. Allow the water to drip off on to kitchen towel and arrange the onion rings on the baking trays in a single layer, spaced apart. Repeat with the remaining onion rings and batter.

4 Spray the onion rings with the cooking spray and bake in the oven for 20–25 minutes, turning halfway through, until golden and crispy, then serve.

Freezing

Open freeze the onion rings on the baking trays at the end of step 3 for 4–6 hours until frozen. Once frozen, divide the onion rings into portions in freezer bags. Seal, label and freeze for up to 3 months.

Serving

Arrange the frozen onion rings in a single layer on a non-stick baking tray and spray with the cooking spray. Cook in a preheated oven at Gas Mark 7/220°C/fan oven 200°C for 20–25 minutes, turning halfway through until golden and crispy.

Rosemary focaccia

These make a perfect accompaniment to the Chicken and Chestnut Mushroom Lasagne on page 28.

ProPoints values per focaccia

ProPoints values per recipe **50**

Makes 12 focaccia

 35 minutes preparation + 1¼ hours proving; 25 minutes cooking

500 g (1 lb 2 oz) strong white bread flour

7 g sachet dried fast action yeast

3 fresh rosemary sprigs, leaves chopped
finely and stems discarded

30 g (1¼ oz) stoned black olives in brine,
chopped finely

calorie controlled cooking spray

½ teaspoon flaked sea salt

1 Reserve 2 tablespoons of flour for kneading. Put the remaining flour in a bowl with the yeast, rosemary and olives. Gradually add 300 ml (10 fl oz) hand-hot water. Mix together until a smooth dough is formed. Dust a work surface with half the reserved flour and knead the dough for 10 minutes until smooth. Spray the bowl with the cooking spray and add the dough. Cover tightly with cling film and leave to prove for 1 hour in a warm place.

2 Remove the cling film and punch down the dough to knock back. Divide the dough in half and roll out each piece on a lightly floured surface (using the reserved flour) until about 20 × 25 cm (8 × 10 inches). Cut each half into six equal pieces.

3 Transfer the dough pieces to two large baking trays lined with non-stick baking parchment. With a lightly floured finger, prod the dough pieces all over to make shallow dimples. Spray with the cooking spray and sprinkle with salt.

4 Loosely cover the trays with cling film and leave to prove for 15 minutes. Preheat the oven to Gas Mark 5/190°C/fan oven 170°C. Remove the cling film and bake the focaccia rolls for 20–25 minutes until golden and risen. They should sound hollow when tapped on the base. Serve while warm, or leave to go cold.

Freezing

At the end of step 3, open freeze the focaccia rolls on a baking tray for 4–6 hours. Then wrap each one in cling film or in freezer bags. Seal, label and freeze for up to 3 months.

Serving

Remove the focaccia rolls from the freezer, put on a lined baking tray and leave to defrost for 45 minutes, then cook as per step 4.

Cheesy potato skins

A sure winner and a great way to use up leftover bits of ham and cheese.

ProPoints values per skin	**3** ProPoints value
ProPoints values per recipe	18
Makes 6 skins	

20 minutes preparation
1½ hours cooking

3 × 200 g (7 oz) floury potatoes**, such as
Maris Piper, scrubbed**
**50 g (1¾ oz) reduced fat mature Cheddar
cheese, grated**
50 g (1¾ oz) lean wafer thin ham**,
chopped roughly**
2 tablespoons finely sliced fresh chives
calorie controlled cooking spray
salt and freshly ground black pepper

1 Preheat the oven to Gas Mark 4/180°C/fan oven 160°C. Prick the potatoes all over with a fork and put on a baking tray. Bake in the oven for 1 hour.

2 Meanwhile, in a bowl, mix together the cheese, ham, chives and seasoning. When the potatoes have baked, allow them to cool slightly and then cut each potato in half. Using a spoon, scoop out the potato, leaving a 1 cm (½ inch) border. Mix the scooped out potato into the cheese mixture.

3 Arrange the potato skins back on the baking tray, cut side up, and carefully spoon some of the cheese and ham filling into each skin until all the mixture is used up.

4 Increase the oven temperature to Gas Mark 5/190°C/fan oven 170°C. Spray the potatoes with the cooking spray and bake in the oven for 25–30 minutes until golden and crispy. Serve immediately.

Freezing

At the end of step 3, leave the potatoes to go cold, then wrap each one in cling film and put in freezer bags. Seal, label and freeze for up to 3 months.

Serving

Remove the potato skins from the freezer and cook from frozen as per step 4 for 30–35 minutes until golden and cooked through.

Vegetarian option **Replace the cheese and ham with 50 g (1¾ oz) feta, 2 tablespoons chopped** fresh parsley **and 10 stoned black olives in brine, drained and chopped into the mix for a taste of Greece and the same** ProPoints **values per serving.**

Creamy mashed potato (pictured with Chianti chicken on page 34)

There is no compromise on taste or flavour here and it gives you perfect mash in minutes every time.

ProPoints values per serving	4
ProPoints values per recipe	14
Serves 4	

15 minutes preparation
25 minutes cooking

500 g (1 lb 2 oz) floury potatoes, such as Maris Piper, peeled and cut into medium chunks
15 g (½ oz) low fat spread
50 g (1¾ oz) low fat soft cheese
2 tablespoons skimmed milk
salt and freshly ground black pepper

1 Put the potatoes in a large saucepan and cover with cold water. Bring to the boil, then reduce the heat and simmer for 20–25 minutes until the potatoes are tender. Drain in a colander for 5 minutes.

2 Return the potatoes to the pan and mash with a potato masher until smooth. Add the low fat spread, soft cheese, milk and some seasoning and beat with a wooden spoon until creamy. Serve immediately.

Freezing

Allow the mashed potato to go cold then divide equally into portions between freezer bags or containers. Seal, label and freeze for up to 3 months.

Serving

Defrost thoroughly and put in a pan. Reheat on a low heat for 3–4 minutes, stirring often, until piping hot. If it is looking a little dry, add 1 tablespoon water while heating.

Carrot and swede crush (pictured with Fillet steak on page 42)

This rough mash is a brilliant way to enjoy carrots and swede which the whole family will enjoy.

ProPoints values per serving	1
ProPoints values per recipe	2
Serves 4	

20 minutes preparation
15 minutes cooking

600 g (1 lb 5 oz) swede, peeled and cut into small chunks
300 g (10½ oz) carrots, peeled and cut into small chunks
1 teaspoon dried ground coriander
a little freshly ground nutmeg
15 g (½ oz) low fat spread
salt and freshly ground black pepper

1 Bring a large pan of water to the boil then reduce the heat and add the swede and carrots. Bring back to the boil then reduce the heat and simmer for 15–20 minutes until tender.

2 Drain in a colander and allow to steam dry for 5 minutes. Return to the pan with the coriander, nutmeg and low fat spread then season. With a potato masher, create a rough mash. Serve immediately.

Freezing

Allow the crush to go cold then divide equally into portions between freezer bags or containers. Seal, label and freeze for up to 3 months.

Serving

Defrost thoroughly. Microwave one portion on high for 3–4 minutes, then leave to stand for 1 minute before serving. Or put in a lidded pan with 2 tablespoons water, cover and reheat on a low heat for 5–7 minutes until piping hot.

Stir-fry veggies

Creating your own stir-fry vegetable packs is a great way to use up leftover veg. Serve this dish with the Thai Beef Mussaman on page 46.

ProPoints values per serving

ProPoints values per recipe	9
Serves 4	

25 minutes in total

1 head of broccoli, cut into small florets

calorie controlled cooking spray

300 g (10½ oz) mixed mushrooms, such as chestnut, shiitake and oyster, sliced

1 red pepper, de-seeded and cut into strips

1 yellow pepper, de-seeded and cut into strips

100 g (3½ oz) frozen peas

100 g (3½ oz) frozen soya beans

2 teaspoons toasted sesame oil

4 tablespoons soy sauce

1 Bring a large pan of water to the boil and add the broccoli. Cook for 2 minutes. Drain and then rinse in cold water. Drain thoroughly and set aside.

2 Heat a wok until hot and spray with the cooking spray. Cook the mushrooms for 8–10 minutes until lightly golden and cooked, stirring occasionally. Remove from the pan.

3 Add the broccoli and peppers to the wok and stir-fry for 3–4 minutes until starting to brown. Add the mushrooms, peas and soya beans and continue to cook for 1–2 minutes. Stir in the sesame oil and soy sauce and serve immediately.

Freezing

At the end of step 2, leave the mushrooms to go cold. Then mix together with the broccoli, peppers, frozen peas and frozen soya beans and divide equally between freezer bags or containers. Seal, label and freeze for up to 3 months.

Serving

Heat a wok until hot, and spray with the cooking spray. Cook everything from frozen for 6–8 minutes until piping hot, adding the soy sauce and sesame oil at the end.

Sauces to prepare ahead

Basic sauces used in recipes which can be made ahead and frozen.

Parsley pesto sauce

ProPoints values per serving	1
ProPoints values per recipe	**11**
Makes 250 g (9 oz)	
(10 × 25 ml/1 fl oz ice cubes)	

 5 minutes in total

Put a dry frying pan on a medium heat, add 40 g (1½ oz) pine nuts and cook for 1–2 minutes, stirring, until toasted and golden. Remove and cool. Put three quarters of a 90 g pack **fresh flat leaf parsley**, stalks discarded, in a food processor, or use a hand-held blender, and add 1 **garlic clove**, chopped roughly, and the pine nuts. Whizz until roughly chopped. Add 50 g (1¾ oz) low fat soft cheese and continue to whizz into a coarse paste. Finely chop the remaining parsley leaves then stir in with 15 g (½ oz) Parmesan cheese, grated, and season generously with freshly ground black pepper. Use as required.

Freezing and serving Once the pesto has been made, divide it equally between 10 × 25 ml (1 fl oz) ice cube tray holes and freeze for 4–6 hours. Once frozen, remove from the trays and transfer to a freezer bag. Seal, label and freeze for up to 3 months. Defrost thoroughly and use as required.

The ultimate tomato sauce

ProPoints values per serving	0
ProPoints values per recipe	**1**
Makes 8 × 150 g (5½ oz) portions	

 25 minutes preparation
2 hours cooking

Preheat the oven to Gas Mark 3/170°C/fan oven 150°C. Heat a large, lidded, flame and ovenproof casserole dish over a medium heat and spray generously with calorie controlled cooking spray. Cook 2 **onions**, diced finely, 3 **celery** sticks, trimmed and diced finely, 2 **carrots**, peeled and diced finely, 3 **garlic cloves**, sliced finely, 4 **fresh thyme** sprigs, 2 bay leaves, 1 **fresh rosemary** sprig for 10 minutes, covered, until softened, stirring occasionally. Add 3 × 400 g cans chopped tomatoes, 300 ml (10 fl oz) vegetable stock, 3 tablespoons balsamic vinegar and bring to the boil. Transfer to the oven and cook, uncovered, for 1½–2 hours until really thickened and well reduced. Discard the herb sprigs and bay leaves then whizz with a hand-held blender until smooth. Season with salt and freshly ground black pepper and enjoy.

Freezing and serving Divide the sauce equally between foil trays or containers. Leave to go cold. Seal, label and freeze for up to 3 months. Defrost thoroughly, then use as required or put in a lidded pan, cover and reheat on a low heat for 5–7 minutes until piping hot, stirring occasionally until smooth.

Basic curry sauce

ProPoints values per serving

ProPoints values per recipe	**12**

Makes 2 × 700 ml (1¼ pint) portions (each portion serves 4)

 20 minutes preparation
50 minutes cooking

Score a cross on the base of 3 large **tomatoes** and put in a bowl. Cover with boiling water and leave to sit for 30 seconds. Then drain and plunge into cold water. Carefully peel the skin from each tomato and discard. Cut the tomatoes in half and discard the seeds. Roughly chop the tomatoes and set aside. Heat a wide, lidded saucepan over a medium heat and spray with calorie controlled cooking spray. Cook 2 **onions**, chopped, 2 **garlic cloves**, chopped, 5 cm (2 inches) **fresh root ginger**, peeled and chopped, 2 green **chillies**, deseeded and chopped, for 8–10 minutes, covered, stirring occasionally until softened. Add the tomatoes and 225 g (8 oz) cooking **apples**, peeled, cored and chopped, and cook for a further 10 minutes, covered, stirring occasionally until lightly browned and the apples and tomatoes have softened. Add 50 g (1¾ oz) medium curry powder and 25 g (1 oz) cornflour and cook, uncovered, for 2 minutes. Remove from the heat and gradually stir in 1 litre (1¾ pints) vegetable stock until combined. Return to the heat and stir in 2 teaspoons soft brown sugar and 50 g (1¾ oz) mango chutney. Bring to the boil, then reduce the heat and simmer, covered, for 30 minutes. Whizz with a hand-held blender or leave to cool slightly before transferring to a blender. Whizz until smooth.

Freezing and serving Divide the sauce equally between foil trays or containers then leave to go cold. Seal, label and freeze for up to 3 months. Defrost thoroughly, put in a lidded pan, cover and reheat on a low heat for 5–7 minutes until piping hot.

Fruity sauce

ProPoints values per serving

ProPoints values per recipe	**8**

Serves 10; Makes 500 ml (18 fl oz)

 10 minutes in total

Put 150 g (5½ oz) fresh **raspberries**, 150 g (5½ oz) fresh **blackberries**, 150 g (5½ oz) fresh **strawberries**, hulled and chopped roughly, 50 g (1¾ oz) fresh **blueberries**, 75 g (2¾ oz) caster sugar in a large saucepan with 4 tablespoons of water and gently heat until the sugar has dissolved. Once the sugar has dissolved, increase the heat slightly and cook for 5 minutes until the fruit has just softened. Whizz with a hand-held blender or transfer to a blender and whizz until smooth. Pass through a sieve into a large jug. Discard the seeds and use the sauce as required.

Freezing and serving Once the sauce has been made, divide between small containers, putting 50 ml (2 fl oz) sauce in each. Leave to go cold then seal, label and freeze for up to 3 months. Defrost thoroughly and use as required.

" *I decide for the week what meals to cook, I make a list and I only buy what's on it.* "

Jill Smith Weight Watchers member

Desserts

Normandy apple tarts

All the flavours of the traditional French dessert but in a simpler version that everyone will love. Serve each with 50 g (1¾ oz) hot reduced fat custard for an extra 1 **ProPoints** value per person.

ProPoints values per tart	**4** ProPoints value
ProPoints values per recipe	21
Makes 6 tarts	

15 minutes preparation
25 minutes cooking

125 g (4½ oz) ready-made shortcrust pastry
50 g (1¾ oz) marzipan
2 eating apples, peeled, cored and cut into small cubes
1 teaspoon icing sugar

1 Preheat the oven to Gas Mark 5/190°C/fan oven 170°C. Roll out the pastry on a large piece of non-stick baking parchment until it is 3 mm (1/8 inch) thick. Stamp out six 9 cm (3½ inch) circles using a cutter or saucer, re-rolling the pastry if you need to get six. Use to line a six-hole non-stick muffin tin, pressing the pastry into each hole and right up the sides. It will look very thin, but don't worry. If you have any tears then use the trimmings to plug the gaps.

2 Divide the marzipan into six equal pieces, roll into small balls and flatten each piece into a small disc. Put a disc of marzipan in the base of each pastry case, then top with the apple cubes, piling them high.

3 Bake the tarts in the oven for 20–25 minutes until the pastry is golden and cooked. Remove from the oven, dust with the icing sugar and serve warm or cold.

Freezing

After baking, leave the tarts to go cold, but do not dust them with icing sugar. Arrange the tarts in a freezerproof container, layered with greaseproof paper. Seal, label and freeze for up to 3 months.

Serving

Defrost and heat at Gas Mark 4/180°C/fan oven 160°C, for 10 minutes, until warmed through, then dust with icing sugar to serve.

Chocolate and cherry pavlovas

Crisp on the outside and soft and chewy in the middle with a tasty chocolate hit. You can vary the fruits depending on what's in season. Raspberries and strawberries work really well too.

ProPoints values per pavlova	**4** ProPoints value
ProPoints values per recipe	26
Makes 6 pavlovas	

15 minutes preparation
1½ hours cooking

1 tablespoon cocoa, sieved
¼ kettleful of boiling water
3 egg whites
¼ teaspoon cream of tartar
150 g (5½ oz) caster sugar
6 tablespoons Weight Watchers West
 Country Thick Cream
225 g (8 oz) frozen cherries, defrosted

1 Preheat the oven to Gas Mark 2/150°C/fan oven 130°C and line a baking sheet with non-stick baking parchment. Dissolve the cocoa in 1 tablespoon of boiling water in a small bowl. Set aside.

2 In a clean, grease-free bowl, whisk the egg whites and cream of tartar until stiff peaks form. Continue to whisk and gradually add the sugar a spoonful at a time to make a really thick and glossy meringue. Mix a large spoonful of the meringue into the cocoa mixture, and then fold this back into the meringue until combined, using a metal spoon.

3 Dollop six spoonfuls of the meringue on to the tray, spacing them well apart and using up all the meringue. Using the back of a wet spoon, make a shallow hole in the middle of each meringue to make a nest. Put the meringues in the oven and immediately reduce the temperature to Gas Mark 1/140°C/fan oven 120°C. Cook for 1½ hours until dry on the outside. Turn off the oven and leave the meringues in the oven to go cold.

4 To serve, remove the meringues from the baking parchment and place on a serving plate. Put the cream in the middle of the meringues, top with the cherries and serve immediately.

Freezing

At the end of step 3, leave to go cold, then arrange the meringue nests in a freezerproof container, layered with greaseproof paper. Seal, label and freeze for up to 3 months.

Serving

Defrost and serve as per step 4.

Apple crumble and mincemeat fingers

A cross between apple crumble and mincemeat cake, this warming dessert is simply delicious.

ProPoints values per finger

ProPoints values per recipe   **52**
Makes 12 fingers

 10 minutes preparation + 15 minutes standing; 45 minutes cooking

125 g (4½ oz) **low fat spread**

2 tablespoons **caster sugar**

250 g (9 oz) **self-raising flour**

1 **egg**

150 g (5½ oz) **mincemeat**

½ teaspoon **baking powder**

1 cooking **apple**, peeled, cored and cutinto small cubes

2 tablespoons **skimmed milk**

3 eating **apples**, peeled, cored and sliced thinly

1 Preheat the oven to Gas Mark 4/180°C/fan oven 160°C and line a 20 × 30 cm (8 × 12 inch) tin with non-stick baking parchment.

2 In a bowl, rub together the low fat spread, sugar and flour with your fingertips until it resembles fine breadcrumbs. Remove 100 g (3½ oz) to another bowl and set aside. Add the egg, mincemeat, baking powder, diced cooking apple and milk to the remaining flour mixture and beat well until combined. Spoon the mixture into the tin, spreading with the back of a spoon to make an even layer.

3 Arrange the sliced apples on top and scatter over the reserved flour mixture, pressing down gently. Bake in the oven for 40–45 minutes until light golden. Leave to stand for 15 minutes before cutting into 12 fingers and serving.

Freezing

At the end of step 3, leave to go cold, then arrange the fingers in a freezerproof container, layered with greaseproof paper. Seal, label and freeze for up to 3 months.

Serving

Defrost and warm in an oven preheated to Gas Mark 5/190°C/fan oven 170°C.

St Clement's sponge pudding

This is irresistible served with 1 tablespoon 0% fat Greek yogurt per person, with clementine and lemon zest stirred through, for an extra 1 **ProPoints** value per serving. Add some raspberries, too, for no extra **ProPoints** values.

ProPoints values per serving	**4** ProPoints value
ProPoints values per recipe	34
Serves 8	

10 minutes preparation + cooling
45 minutes cooking

75 g (2¾ oz) low fat spread

1 clementine

½ a kettleful of boiling water

zest of 1 lemon

125 g (4½ oz) self-raising flour

1 level teaspoon baking powder

100 g (3½ oz) caster sugar

2 eggs

1 Preheat the oven to Gas Mark 4/180°C/fan oven 160°C. Grease and line the base of a 20 cm (8 inch) shallow cake tin with 1 teaspoon of the low fat spread and some baking parchment.

2 Put the clementine in a small saucepan, cover with boiling water and simmer until soft, about 20 minutes. Set aside to cool. When the clementine is soft and cool, cut in half and remove any pips. Process the whole clementine in a food processor, including the skin, until it makes a rough purée. Add the remaining cake ingredients and blend until smooth. You can do this with a food processor or transfer the mixture to a bowl and use a hand-held blender. Spoon the mixture into the cake tin and spread to level with the back of a spoon.

3 Bake in the preheated oven for 20–25 minutes, until a skewer comes out clean when inserted into the centre. Serve in wedges.

Freezing

At the end of step 3, allow to cool and cut into wedges or keep the pudding whole. Wrap in cling film and put in a freezer bag. Seal, label and freeze for up to 3 months.

Serving

Defrost and warm at Gas Mark 4/180°C/fan oven 160°C, wrapped in foil, until warm.

Self-saucing chocolate pudding

This pudding has a secret – a devilish chocolate sauce at the bottom. And it's the ideal make one, freeze one recipe.

ProPoints values per serving	5 ProPoints value
ProPoints values per recipe	**38**
Serves 8	

15 minutes preparation + 2 hours chilling; 20 minutes cooking

125 g (4½ oz) plain flour
zest of 1 orange
50 g (1¾ oz) caster sugar
2 teaspoons baking powder
3 tablespoons cocoa, sieved
125 ml (4 fl oz) skimmed milk
40 g (1½ oz) low fat spread, melted
1 egg
75 g (2¾ oz) light muscovado sugar
½ a kettleful of boiling water

1 Put the flour, orange zest, sugar, baking powder and 2 teaspoons of the cocoa in a bowl. Mix together the milk, low fat spread and egg in a large jug and gradually pour into the flour mixture, stirring. Mix until smooth and then divide equally between two 650 ml (22 fl oz) ovenproof dishes. Cover with cling film and chill for 2 hours.

2 Preheat the oven to Gas Mark 4/180°C/fan oven 160°C. In a bowl, mix together the muscovado sugar and remaining cocoa. Sprinkle half of this over the top of each pudding.

3 Pour 100 ml (3½ fl oz) boiling water carefully over each pudding and bake in the oven for 20 minutes until the sponge is springy and the sauce is bubbling.

Freezing

At the end of step 2, seal, label and freeze for up to 3 months.

Serving

Cook as per step 3, for 25–30 minutes.

Simple pear strudel

Serve warm with a 60 g (2 oz) scoop of low fat vanilla ice cream per person for an extra 2 **ProPoints** values per serving.

ProPoints values per serving	4 ProPoints value
ProPoints values per recipe	23
Serves 6	

 10 minutes preparation
45 minutes cooking

2 firm pears, peeled, cored and diced
1 cooking apple, peeled, cored and diced
25 g (1 oz) sultanas
15 g (½ oz) pecans, chopped
25 g (1 oz) caster sugar
2 teaspoons mixed spice
4 × 45 g (1½ oz) sheets fresh filo pastry,
**   measuring 50 × 24 cm (20 ×**
**   9½ inches)**
calorie controlled cooking spray
1 tablespoon dried breadcrumbs
1 teaspoon icing sugar

1 Preheat the oven to Gas Mark 5/190°C/fan oven 170°C. Put the pears, apple, sultanas, pecans, sugar and mixed spice in a lidded saucepan and cook gently over a low heat, covered, for 15 minutes until softened. Leave to go cold.

2 Put a sheet of filo pastry on a large piece of baking parchment and spray with the cooking spray. Top with another sheet and spray again. Repeat with the remaining sheets. Sprinkle the breadcrumbs over the pastry and then spread the pear mixture over the top, leaving a 2 cm (¾ inch) border.

3 Roll up the pastry along the long edge like a Swiss roll. Seal the ends by pressing together the pastry then bend into a horseshoe shape. Score the top of the strudel with a knife about six times and spray with the cooking spray.

4 Bake in the oven for 20–30 minutes until golden. Dust with icing sugar and serve in slices.

Freezing

At the end of step 3, carefully wrap in baking parchment and foil. Seal, label and freeze for up to 3 months.

Serving

Defrost and cook as per step 4 until piping hot.

Cook's tip You can vary the nuts according to what you have available. Walnuts work really well too, for the same **ProPoints** values per serving.

Frozen raspberry terrine

This is a bit like that good old favourite, trifle, but frozen in a loaf tin instead. The kirsch helps to bring out the raspberry flavour, but you can use sherry instead of the kirsch if you prefer.

ProPoints values per serving	**3** ProPoints value
ProPoints values per recipe	23
Serves 8	

15 minutes preparation
4 hours freezing

300 g (10½ oz) frozen or fresh raspberries

200 g (7 oz) low fat vanilla ice cream

300 g pot Weight Watchers reduced fat fresh custard

3 tablespoons kirsch

12 sponge fingers

1 Rinse a standard size loaf tin (where the base measures about 20 × 8 cm/8 × 3¼ inches) with cold water and then line the sides and base with baking paper, leaving a little overhang. Mash 125 g (4½ oz) of the raspberries in a bowl, then transfer them to a sieve set over another bowl and push through to make a purée, using the back of a spoon. Discard the seeds.

2 In a separate large bowl, working quickly, mash together the ice cream and custard. Put the kirsch in another bowl.

3 Working quickly, spoon a third of the ice cream mix into the base of the loaf tin and spread with the back of a spoon to cover the base. Drizzle with a third of the raspberry purée. Dip six sponge fingers, one at a time, into the kirsch and arrange in the tin, spaced apart. Sprinkle over half the raspberries into the gaps. Repeat these layers, then finish with the final third of the ice cream mixture and drizzle with the purée. Wrap the top with foil and freeze for 4 hours.

4 To serve, remove the terrine from the loaf tin by turning upside down on to a platter and discarding the paper. Cut into slices and serve immediately.

Freezing
At the end of step 3, keep in the freezer for up to 3 months.

Serving
Defrost in the fridge for 30 minutes before slicing.

Raspberry sorbet

This is seriously bursting with raspberry flavour. Serve 65 g (2¼ oz) scoops on their own or with other fruit such as strawberries and blueberries for no additional **ProPoints** values.

ProPoints values per serving	**2** ProPoints value
ProPoints values per recipe	17
Serves 8	

15 minutes preparation
8–10 hours freezing

150 g (5½ oz) caster sugar
¼ kettleful of boiling water
juice of 1 lemon
400 g (14 oz) fresh raspberries
1 egg white

1 Dissolve the sugar in 150 ml (5 fl oz) boiling water from the kettle, stirring well. Add the lemon juice. Add the raspberries to the sugar syrup and whizz to a purée with a hand-held blender. Pass the purée through a sieve into a jug to remove the seeds.

2 Pour the purée into a 500 ml (18 fl oz) shallow container, such as a freezerproof baking dish. Cover with cling film then freeze for 4–6 hours or until the mixture is frozen.

3 Whisk the egg white until it forms stiff peaks. Remove the sorbet from the freezer and cut it into rough chunks. Whizz these chunks in a food processor or with a hand-held blender until smooth. Transfer to the egg white and fold together gently.

4 Pour the mixture back into the freezerproof container and freeze for at least 4 hours or overnight. Serve as desired.

Freezing

Keep the raspberry sorbet in the freezer for up to 3 months.

Serving

Serve straight from the freezer.

Arctic roll

This home-made version of a schoolday classic is so easy to make. Serve with fresh raspberries on the side for no extra **ProPoints** values.

ProPoints values per serving	**4** ProPoints value
ProPoints values per recipe	37
Serves 10	

 20 minutes preparation; 10 minutes cooking; 1 hour freezing

300 g (10½ oz) low fat vanilla ice cream
3 eggs
75 g (2¾ oz) caster sugar, plus
    1 tablespoon for dusting
75 g (2¾ oz) self-raising flour
75 g (2¾ oz) seedless raspberry jam
Fruity Sauce (page 121), to serve
    (optional)

1 Preheat the oven to Gas Mark 6/200°C/fan oven 180°C and line a 23 × 30 cm (9 × 12 inch) Swiss roll tin with non-stick baking parchment. Spoon the ice cream on to a sheet of cling film in a long line, then wrap with the cling film and quickly roll into a sausage until it is about 23 cm (9 inches) long. Put the ice cream roll in the freezer.

2 In a medium bowl, whisk the eggs and sugar with an electric hand whisk until pale, fluffy and really thick. Carefully fold in the flour and spoon into the prepared tin, tipping the tin to spread the mixture evenly. Bake in the oven for 7–10 minutes or until light golden and springy to the touch. Remove from the oven and turn the sponge out on to a piece of baking parchment that has been dusted with the remaining tablespoon of caster sugar.

3 Roll up the sponge like a Swiss roll. Start at the long edge and roll up the baking parchment with it to prevent it from sticking together. Leave to go cold. Carefully unroll the sponge and discard the baking parchment. Spread the sponge with the jam, leaving a 1 cm (½ inch) border, then take the ice cream roll from the freezer and remove and discard the cling film. Arrange the ice cream roll along the centre of the sponge. Working quickly, roll the sponge up and wrap in foil. Freeze for at least 1 hour and then serve as required with Fruity Sauce, if liked.

Freezing
Keep in the freezer for up to 3 months.

Serving
Cut a slice straight from the freezer.

Index

V denotes a vegetarian recipe